Nelson Advanced Modular Science

Microorganisms and Biotechnology

JOHN ADDS • ERICA LARKCOM • RUTH MILLER

Nelson

Thomas Nelson & Sons Ltd
Nelson House
Mayfield Road
Walton-on-Thames
Surrey KT12 5PL
United Kingdom

I(T)P   Thomas Nelson is an International Thomson Company
I(T)P   is used under licence

First Published by Thomas Nelson & Sons Ltd 1998
ISBN   0 17 448269 8
9 8 7 6 5 4 3 2 1
01 00 99 98

Typesetting and illustration by Hardlines, Charlbury, Oxfordshire
Printed in Croatia by Zrinski Printing and Publishing House, Cakovec
Picture Research by Image Select International Ltd

Publication team:
Acquisitions: Sonia Clark
Editorial Management: Simon Bell
Freelance Editorial: Liz Jones
Production: Suzanne Howarth
Marketing: Jane Lewis

Acknowledgements

The authors and publishers would like to thank the following
for permission to reproduce copyright material.

Photographs

Science Photo Library: figures 1.1 (top) Dr Kari Lounatmaa
/SPL; 1.1 (upper middle) Eye of Science/SPL; 1.1
(lower middle) Eric Grave/SPL; 1.1 (bottom) Chris Bjornberg
/SPL; 1.3 Dr L. Caro/SPL; 1.5 Dr Kari Lounatmaa/SPL; 1.6
Dr D.A. Stetler/SPL; 1.8 Manfred Kage/SPL; 1.11 Barry Dowsett
/SPL; 1.14 Astrid and Hanns-Frieder Michler/SPL; 1.15
Dr P. Marazzi/SPL; 2.11 Sinclair Stammers/SPL. Erica Larkcom:
figures 3.1; 3.3a, b and c; 3.15b and c; 3.17; 3.20; 3.33 a and b;
3.36 a, b and c, Neil Thompson: figures 2.2 and 3.25,
The Babraham Institute: figure 3.2, Michael Busselle/Tony Stone
Images: figure 3.11, English National Hop Association:
figure 3.13, Chris Fairclough/Image Select: figure 3.14, J.Alan
Cash: figure 3.15a, Ann Ronan/Image Select figure 3.23, Ruth
Miller: figure 3.35.

Artwork and other material

Dean Madden, National Centre for Biotechnology Education,
Reading University: figure 1.13 (original appeared in NCBE's
'The lambda protocol'; figures 2.10, 3.4, 3.8, 3.21 and 3.22
(from NCBE newsletters); figure 3.5 (original in EIBE, Unit 1);
table 3.1 (modified from NCBE poster); figure 3.37 (from
'Food biotechnology – an introduction'); 'Use of immobilised
enzymes' practical, page 79, (first published in Warwick
Process Science , 1986) John Schollar, National Centre for
Biotechnology Education, Reading University: figure 2.8

Contents

Introduction

As modularisation of syllabuses gains momentum, there is a corresponding demand for a modular format in supporting texts. The Nelson Advanced Modular Science series has been written by Chief and Principal Examiners and those involved directly with the A level examinations. The books are based on the London Examinations (Edexcel) AS and A level modular syllabuses in Biology and Human Biology, Chemistry and Physics. Each module text offers complete and self-contained coverage of all the topics in the module. The texts also include examples outside the prescribed syllabus to broaden your understanding and help to illustrate the principle which is being presented. There are practical investigations and regular review questions to stimulate your thinking while you read about and study the topic. Finally, there are typical examination questions with mark schemes so that you can test yourself and help you to understand how to approach the examination.

In the Option modules of the London syllabuses, we explore applications of Biology, delving into some areas where we really make use of biology in society. Microorganisms and Biotechnology looks at a selection of microorganisms, chosen to illustrate how microbes interact with human lives. The diversity of microorganisms is appreciated through a representative range of bacteria, fungi, viruses and protoctists. While some of these microbes are familiar as agents of disease, others have been used by humans through the centuries, often to provide food and drink. From ancient biotechnology to the modern food industry, we see how enzymes and microorganisms have been and are exploited in the modification of foods. We look also at examples of ways that microorganisms and biotechnology are utilised in medical care and in agriculture, and this then gives us a glimpse into the future potential of gene technology. Appropriate practical techniques are described for use on a laboratory scale, providing an understanding of the essentials for culture of microorganisms in large scale industrial production. The authors hope that through your study of biology, you can appreciate how the activities of microorganisms and applications of biotechnology are of considerable importance to society – now and in the future. If our speculation is correct, it is this area of biology that will expand considerably as we move into the 21st century.

The authors

Erica Larkcom B.A., M.A., C.Biol., M.I.Biol., former Subject Officer for A level Biology, former Head of Biology, Great Cornard Upper School, Suffolk

John Adds B.A., C.Biol., M.I.Biol., Dip.Ed., Chief Examiner for A level Biology, Head of Biology, Abbey Tutorial College, London

Ruth Miller B.Sc., C.Biol., M.I.Biol., Chief Examiner for AS and A level Biology, former Head of Biology, Sir William Perkins's School, Chertsey, Surrey

Note to teachers on safety

When practical instructions have been given we have attempted to indicate hazardous substances and operations by using standard symbols and appropriate precautions. Nevertheless you should be aware of your obligations under the Health and Safety at Work Act, Control of Substances Hazardous to Health (COSHH) Regulations and the Management of Health and Safety at Work Regulations. In this respect you should follow the requirements of your employers at all times.

In carrying out practical work, students should be encouraged to carry out their own risk assessments, i.e. they should identify hazards and suitable ways of reducing the risks from them. However they must be checked by the teacher/lecturer. Students should also know what to do in an emergency, such as a fire.

The teachers/lecturers should be familiar and up to date with current advice from professional bodies.

The range of microorganisms: microorganisms and disease

Introduction

The term **microorganism** is widely used to describe an organism which is too small to be seen without using a microscope. It is an imprecise term, as such organisms do not possess any other common features, apart from the fact that they are usually single-celled. They are found within a range of taxonomic groups, many of which also include larger, multicellular organisms. It is generally agreed that all the **bacteria** (kingdom **Prokaryotae**) are microorganisms and that the term can also be applied to the unicellular, heterotrophic **protozoa** and the unicellular **algae** found within the kingdom **Protoctista**, and to members of the kingdom **Fungi**, such as filamentous moulds and the yeasts. **Viruses** fulfil some of the criteria, in that they are very small, but differ in lacking a cellular structure with no organised nucleus (**akaryote**) and being dependent on other cells for their reproduction. Their effect on other living organisms is often profound, although some viral infections of plants seem to have little effect.

Most interest in microorganisms is centred around those which can be exploited to produce useful products and those which are pathogenic to human beings, domesticated animals and plant crops. Microorganisms have been used for thousands of years in the production of food and beverages. The Babylonians were making beer, possibly by 8 000 BP, leavened bread was being baked by the Egyptians in 6 000 BP and there are references in the Old Testament of the Bible to wine being made. However, it was not until the simple microscope was developed by Antonie van Leeuwenhoek in the 17th century, that microorganisms were first seen and described. In the 19th century, Louis Pasteur demonstrated that microorganisms could bring about fermentation and by the end of that century, some alcohols were being produced commercially. Engineering techniques were used to develop ways of culturing microorganisms on a larger scale and by the 1940s, antibiotic production, involving the necessity for sterile conditions, had been achieved. A significant step was the ability to isolate pure cultures of microorganisms. In the 1960s and 1970s, a greater knowledge of the genetics of microorganisms lead to the selection of more productive strains. More recently, it has become possible to use applied genetics and the techniques of recombinant DNA technology to alter the genetic constitution of microorganisms and so improve the traditional strains used in industrial processes.

If we include viruses as microorganisms, then three levels of organisation, or cell structure, can be distinguished:
- **prokaryotic** – as shown by bacteria
- **eukaryotic** – as shown by the protoctistans (unicellular protozoa and unicellular algae) and the fungi (yeasts and moulds)
- **viruses** – consisting only of nucleic acid and proteins, sometimes referred to as akaryotic.

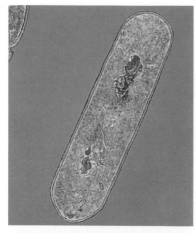

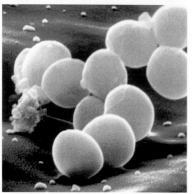

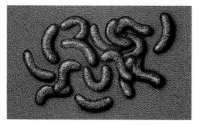

Figure 1.1 Representatives of the four basic categories of bacteria: (top) Bacillus licheniformis, which can be isolated from soil or air and produces an antibiotic called bacitracin; (upper middle) Staphylococcus aureus, which causes skin infections in humans; (lower middle) Spirillum volutans, one of the largest bacteria, occurring in stagnant freshwater; (bottom) Vibrio cholerae, the bacterium that causes cholera

Microorganisms range in size from those which are just about visible to the naked eye, such as some of the larger protoctistans, to those which can only be seen using an electron microscope. Most eukaryotic cells have a diameter between 10 and 30 μm (micrometres), whereas the diameter of bacterial cells may range from 0.2 to 2.0 μm and viruses from 20 to 300 nm (nanometres). The internal structure of bacterial cells and the structure of viruses are only visible using electron microscopy. The sizes of a range of microorganisms are shown in Table 1.1.

Table 1.1 *The sizes of some microorganisms*

Type of microorganism	Size in μm (micrometres)
Amoeba sp. (Protoctista / protozoan)	150 to 200
Chlorella sp. (Protoctista / alga)	20
Saccharomyces sp. (Fungi / yeast)	10
Escherichia coli (Prokaryotae / bacterium)	1.0
poliomyelitis virus	0.02
tobacco mosaic virus	0.015

Prokaryotes and eukaryotes

Bacteria are prokaryotic and they differ in structure and organisation from other groups of microorganisms. The major differences are summarised in Table 1.2.

Bacteria

When bacteria are viewed using light microscopy, it is impossible to discern any details of their structure apart from their shape. For this reason, the earliest attempts at a classification grouped the bacteria into the following categories:
- **bacilli** (singular **bacillus**) – rod-shaped, e.g. *Bacillus*
- **cocci** (singular **coccus**) – spherical, e.g. *Staphylococcus*
- **spirilla** (singular **spirillum**) – spiral, e.g. *Spirillum*
- **vibrio** – comma-shaped, e.g. *Vibrio*

This system was extended by determining whether the cells remained single, or formed chains or clusters, and whether or not flagella were present.

Many bacteria can alter their shape as a result of ageing, or due to an environmental shock such as a rapid change in temperature – a phenomenon known as **pleomorphy**. This can cause confusion in the identification of species if only morphological features are used. With the development of the electron microscope, it has been possible to determine the internal organisation of bacterial cells, but their structure is remarkably similar. All bacteria possess:
- a rigid cell wall
- a cell surface membrane
- cytoplasm
- a double-stranded loop of DNA (the bacterial chromosome)
- small (70S) ribosomes
- storage granules of glycogen and lipid droplets.

Table 1.2 *Major differences between prokaryotic and eukaryotic microorganisms*

Prokaryotes	Eukaryotes
rigid cell wall usually present; contains peptidoglycan (murein)	cell walls, when present, contain cellulose (*Chlorella*) or chitin (*Saccharomyces*)
no true nucleus	true nucleus present, surrounded by nuclear envelope with pores
circular DNA; bacterial chromosome lacks histones; may be additional, separate circular pieces of DNA called plasmids carrying non-essential genes	linear DNA with associated histone proteins, forming true chromosomes
no membrane-bound organelles; lack mitochondria, but mesosomes in some bacteria for respiration; lack chloroplasts, but thylakoids (photosynthetic membranes) present in photosynthetic bacteria	many membrane-bound organelles; mitochondria for aerobic respiration; chloroplasts with lamellae in photosynthetic organisms
no endoplasmic reticulum; no Golgi apparatus, lysosomes or vacuoles	endoplasmic reticulum present with associated Golgi apparatus, lysosomes and vacuoles
small (70S) ribosomes scattered in the cytoplasm	larger (80S) ribosomes with some located on internal membranes
cell surface membrane infoldings (invaginations) may form mesosomes and thylakoids; allow passage of large molecules such as fragments of DNA, but endocytosis not seen and no microvilli present	endocytosis and exocytosis may occur through cell surface membrane; microvilli may be present
flagella, when present, lack microtubules	flagella, when present, have 9 + 2 arrangement of microtubules
reproduction asexual only; binary fission or budding; no sexual reproduction as such but exchange of genetic material may occur	reproduction may be sexual or asexual; most eukaryotic microorganisms are haploid; gamete formation occurs by mitosis, fertilisation results in a diploid zygote which undergoes meiosis, restoring the haploid condition

In some bacteria the outer surface of the cell wall may be coated with a **glycocalyx**, which can take the form of a **slime layer** or a thicker, more structured **capsule**. Slime layers form loose, soluble coverings that are easily washed off, whereas capsules, which may be composed of polysaccharides, polypeptides or a mixture of both, are bound more tightly to the cell wall and have a more 'gummy' consistency. Any gelatinous covering will form a protective barrier between the bacterium and the external environment. It will reduce the chances of desiccation and cause the cells to stick together. In pathogenic bacteria, the capsule prevents antibodies and phagocytic blood corpuscles from binding to the cell wall. The bacterial cell walls are not destroyed and the bacteria are able to multiply within the host and infect the body tissues. Slime layers help bacteria to adhere to each other and to surfaces, enabling colonisation. The slime layers present in many soil bacteria contribute to the binding of soil particles, creating a good 'crumb' structure.

Many bacteria possess **flagella** (singular: **flagellum**). These may occur all over the cell, limited to a group at one or both ends, or singly.

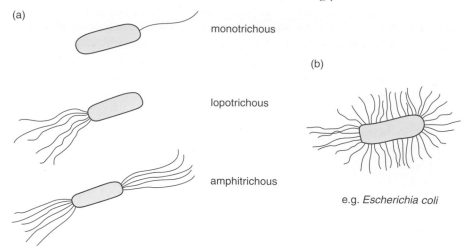

Figure 1.2 Different positions in which flagella occur in bacteria (a) polar attachment – flagella attached at one or both ends; (b) peritrichous attachment – flagella dispersed randomly over surface of cell

As already mentioned, bacterial flagella differ from those in eukaryotic organisms. Each bacterial flagellum consists of a single filament formed from a hollow cylinder of helically arranged molecules of the protein flagellin. Flagella confer motility and enable bacteria to show **chemotaxis**, responding to chemical stimuli by moving towards favourable conditions or away from unfavourable ones.

Pili and **fimbriae** are projections from the cell surface membrane through the cell wall. They occur in some bacteria and differ from flagella, both in their structure and their function. They are composed of a protein called pilin and, being more rigid than flagella, are concerned with attachment to other bacteria or to host cells, rather than with locomotion. Fimbriae are short and bristle-like, whereas the pili are longer and less numerous. They are both antigenic and attachment often involves interaction with the molecules of host-cell membranes. In pathogenic bacteria, the presence of large numbers of fimbriae may help to prevent phagocytosis by host cells. The longer pili are found in some Gram-negative bacteria, where they are associated with the process of **conjugation**, in which exchange of genetic material occurs.

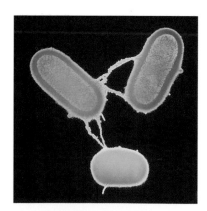

Figure 1.3 Three E. coli bacteria linked by pili. One bacterium is donating DNA through the pili to the other two, transforming them

The bacterial cell wall is largely composed of a mixed polymer of hexose sugars and amino acids called **peptidoglycan**, sometimes referred to as **mucopeptide** or **murein**. The peptidoglycans provide a strong but flexible framework, supporting the cell contents and protecting the bacterial cell from lysis. The effectiveness of certain drugs in the treatment of bacterial infections depends on their ability to destroy or prevent the synthesis of peptidoglycan, thus weakening the cell wall and enabling lysis to occur. **Lysozyme**, a naturally-occurring enzyme present in tears and saliva, hydrolyses peptidoglycan and provides defence against some bacteria. Damage to bacterial cell walls can also be caused by some disinfectants.

In 1884, a Danish doctor, Hans Christian Gram, developed a staining technique which he used in an attempt to enable pathogenic species of bacteria to be more quickly identified. The technique involves the application of a dye, **crystal violet**, to a bacterial smear on a microscope slide. The slide is then flooded with **Gram's iodine** (iodine in potassium iodide solution) to intensify the crystal violet, by causing it to form large crystals. The preparations are then rinsed in alcohol and counterstained with the red dye, **safranin**. Bacteria with thick peptidoglycan walls retain the crystal violet which does not get washed out when alcohol is added. In such bacteria, counterstaining with safranin has no effect and they are termed **Gram positive** bacteria. In bacteria with thinner walls, containing less peptidoglycan, the alcohol dissolves the lipids on the surface and then removes the dye from the peptidoglycan layer. Counterstaining with safranin leaves such cells stained pink. These bacteria are termed **Gram negative**.

The Gram stain is still a useful technique in the classification of bacteria and provides a rapid means for the initial identification of pathogenic species. Electron microscopy has revealed the nature of the differences in cell-wall structure between Gram positive and Gram negative bacteria. These are summarised in Table 1.3 and Figure 1.4.

Table 1.3 *Differences in cell wall structure between Gram positive and Gram negative bacteria*

Feature	Gram positive bacteria	Gram negative bacteria
overall thickness	20 to 80 nm	8 to 11 nm
thickness of peptidoglycan layer	20 to 80 nm	1 to 2 nm
outer membrane with lipoprotein and protein lipopolysaccharides present	no	yes
channels present spanning outer membrane (porins)	no	yes
space between cell surface membrane and cell wall (periplasmic space)	sometimes present	always present

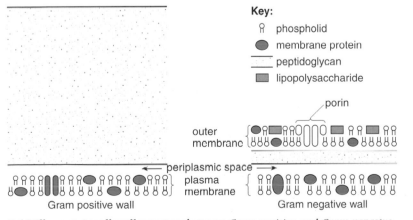

Key:
- ⚲ phospholid
- ⬤ membrane protein
- ▭ peptidoglycan
- ▣ lipopolysaccharide

porin

outer membrane

periplasmic space

plasma membrane

Gram positive wall   Gram negative wall

Figure 1.4 Differences in cell wall structure between Gram positive and Gram negative bacteria

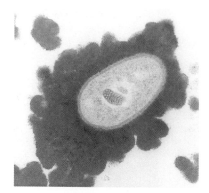

Figure 1.5 TEM through a skin bacterium showing the mesosome

Figure 1.6 TEM of thylakoids in a chloroplast

In Gram-negative bacteria, the outer membrane forms an extra barrier making them more impervious to disinfectants and dyes, although alcohol can dissolve the lipids.

The bacterial cell surface membrane is composed of a lipid bilayer with protein molecules embedded in it. It is very similar to the cell surface membranes of eukaryotic organisms, except that there is a higher ratio of protein to phospholipid molecules. The major functions are control of the transport of substances into and out of the cell, secretion and metabolic activities. Most of the enzymes concerned with respiration are located here, as are enzyme systems concerned with the synthesis of structural molecules. The membrane also secretes enzymes and toxins into the outside environment.

In some Gram positive bacteria, it can be seen quite clearly that the cell surface membrane is extensively infolded (invaginated) forming a **mesosome**. Although there is some debate as to the precise nature of such structures, it is generally agreed that there is an increase in the surface area available for metabolic activities. It is thought that the mesosomes may be involved with cell wall synthesis and that they may play a role in cell division, in addition to increasing the surface area available for the generation of ATP. Mesosomes may also be present in Gram negative bacteria, but they are less easily seen due to their small size. In photosynthetic bacteria, the cell surface membrane is invaginated to form **thylakoids**, on which are found pigment molecules and associated enzymes.

The cytoplasm of bacterial cells is largely composed of water, together with sugars, amino acids and salts. Also present are inclusions such as glycogen granules, lipid droplets and polyhydroxybutyric acid (PHB), all of which are energy-rich storage molecules. Some aquatic bacteria possess gas vesicles, which provide buoyancy, and many also have crystals of inorganic compounds.

Large numbers of **ribosomes** are present in bacterial cells. They are either scattered singly in the cytoplasm or arranged in chains, forming polysomes. These ribosomes are the sites of protein synthesis and function in exactly the same way as the ribosomes in eukaryotic organisms, but they are smaller and lighter (70S as opposed to 80S).

Endospore formation occurs in some Gram positive genera. Endospores are dormant structures which develop in response to a change in environmental conditions, such as depletion of nutrients. The protoplasm becomes surrounded by a thick, impervious coat, which protects the contents from desiccation and which is resistant to radiation and toxic chemicals. When favourable conditions return, the endospore germinates and vegetative growth is restored. *Bacillus anthracis*, the organism responsible for anthrax, forms endospores, which are known to retain their viability for 50 years.

Bacterial **DNA** is in the form of a ring, called the **chromatin body** or **bacterial chromosome**. The DNA molecule is very long and tightly coiled around basic protein molecules. There are no histone proteins associated with the DNA and there is no nuclear envelope surrounding it. The genes present on this bacterial chromosome are those necessary for growth and maintenance. In addition, many bacteria contain smaller, circular pieces of extra-chromosomal DNA called **plasmids**. These may either be free in the cytoplasm or attached to the bacterial chromosome, but they are independent and self-replicating. The genes on the plasmids are not essential for the growth or metabolism of the bacterial cell, but may be concerned with the production of sex pili, confer resistance to drugs or produce toxins and enzymes. When the bacterial cell undergoes binary fission, the plasmids are duplicated and passed on to the daughter cells. Modern techniques in gene (DNA) technology enable such plasmids to be manipulated in the laboratory and they provide a valuable means of introducing additional genetic information into bacterial cells.

As indicated earlier in this chapter, identification and classification of bacteria are difficult. We have considered some of the morphological features which are used, but precise identification may require the use of other characteristics. Table 1.4 summarises some of the additional ways which may be used to identify and classify bacteria.

Table 1.4 *Summary of methods of identification and classification of bacteria*

Method	Description and comments
microscopic morphology	use of cell shape, size, Gram staining; presence of flagella, pili, fimbriae, capsules, endospores
macroscopic morphology	appearance of colony in broth or on solid media; texture, size, rate of growth, pigmentation
biochemical characteristics	ability to ferment certain sugars; breakdown specific proteins or polysaccharides; produce gases, for example
chemical characteristics	presence of certain compounds in the cell wall and membrane
presence of specific antigens	antibodies are produced in response to specific antigens; useful in the identification of pathogens in specimens and cultures
use of genetic probes	small single-stranded fragments of DNA (probes), labelled with a dye or a radioactive isotope, are mixed with unknown DNA; if there is a match, hybridisation occurs; probes become attached to unknown DNA and can show up

Fungi – yeasts and moulds

Fungi are eukaryotic organisms that:
- form spores
- lack flagella at any stage in their life cycle
- do not possess chlorophyll
- usually have chitin in their cell walls.

They may be single-celled, as in the yeasts (*Saccharomyces*) or more usually filamentous, as in moulds such as *Penicillium*. The kingdom is divided into phyla, which differ from each other in the nature of their spore producing structures. Both *Saccharomyces* and *Penicillium* belong to the phylum Ascomycota.

In the **filamentous moulds**, individual filaments are called **hyphae** (singular: **hypha**) and develop directly from spores. There is no embryonic stage in the life cycle. The hyphae grow together, forming a loose network of threads called a **mycelium**. The hyphal walls are normally chitinous and divided into cell-like compartments by cross walls, or **septa** (singular: **septum**). The hyphae contain cytoplasm in which are situated one or two nuclei per 'cell'. Each nucleus is surrounded by a nuclear envelope and organelles such as mitochondria, ribosomes and Golgi bodies are also present in the cytoplasm. There are pores in the septa so that the cytoplasm is continuous in each hypha, making cell-to-cell communication possible.

Most fungi are terrestrial and saprobiontic, feeding on the dead and decaying remains of plants and animals. When grown in the laboratory, fungi need to be supplied with organic sources of carbon and nitrogen, together with inorganic ions and one or more vitamins. Digestive enzymes are secreted from the hyphae on to the food material and the soluble products of this **extra-cellular digestion** are absorbed. Growth of the mycelium is concentrated at the tips of the hyphae where the cytoplasm is dense and most metabolic activity is occurring. In the older parts of the mycelium, vacuoles develop and the cytoplasm is restricted to the periphery of the hyphae.

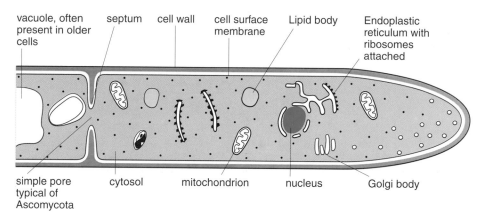

Figure 1.7 Structure of fungal hypha

The yeasts are single-celled fungi, which do not usually form hyphae. The genus *Saccharomyces* is of economic importance in the fermentation processes associated with the baking and brewing industries.

Yeast cells are ellipsoidal to spherical in shape. Each is surrounded by a wall containing polymers of the sugars glucose and mannose. In the cytoplasm, the nucleus is usually situated to one side of a large central vacuole. In addition to the other membrane-bound organelles typical of eukaryotic cells, there are usually storage granules of glycogen and the vacuole may contain lipid droplets and polyphosphate granules. *Saccharomyces* reproduces asexually by budding, during which process a daughter cell develops as an outgrowth from one end of a parent cell. When the daughter cell detaches, a scar is left, which is visible as an indentation on the parent cell wall.

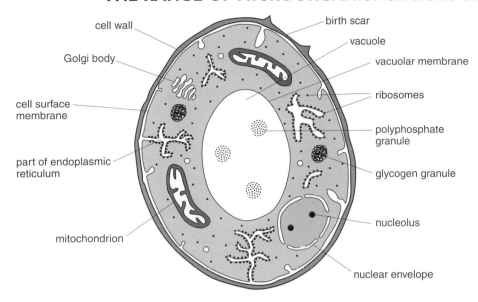

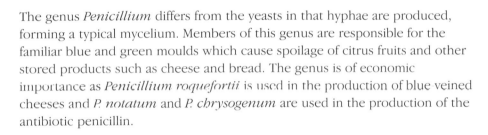

cell wall

Golgi body

cell surface membrane

part of endoplasmic reticulum

mitochondrion

birth scar

vacuole

vacuolar membrane

ribosomes

polyphosphate granule

glycogen granule

nucleolus

nuclear envelope

Figure 1.8 (a) Electronmicrograph drawing of a section of a yeast cell

Figure 1.8 (b) scanning electronmicrograph of yeast cells

The genus *Penicillium* differs from the yeasts in that hyphae are produced, forming a typical mycelium. Members of this genus are responsible for the familiar blue and green moulds which cause spoilage of citrus fruits and other stored products such as cheese and bread. The genus is of economic importance as *Penicillium roquefortii* is used in the production of blue-veined cheeses and *P. notatum* and *P. chrysogenum* are used in the production of the antibiotic penicillin.

Penicillium species can be distinguished from other moulds by the characteristic appearance of the asexual spores, the **conidiospores**, which are formed on special aerial branches of the mycelium called **conidiophores**. The conidiospores develop in chains from **sterigma** at the tips of the conidiophores and as they are very light, they are easily dispersed in air currents when dislodged.

Protoctists

The kingdom Protoctista contains a large number of eukaryotic organisms which are considered to be microorganisms, including the unicellular algae. Algae differ from most other groups in this kingdom in that they are photosynthetic. They all possess chlorophyll *a*, together with a variety of other photosynthetic pigments characteristic of the different phyla to which they belong.

Chlorella is a genus of unicellular green algae classified in the phylum Chlorophyta. It possesses a single, cup-shaped chloroplast (chromatophore) containing photosynthetic pigments similar to those present in green plants. The cells are surrounded by thin, cellulose cell walls, there are starch grains and oil droplets in the cytoplasm and a crystalline structure, called a pyrenoid, is embedded in the chloroplast. This structure is concerned with the formation of starch.

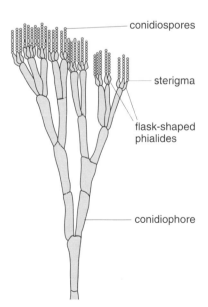

conidiospores

sterigma

flask-shaped phialides

conidiophore

Figure 1.9 The structure of Penicillium *sp.*

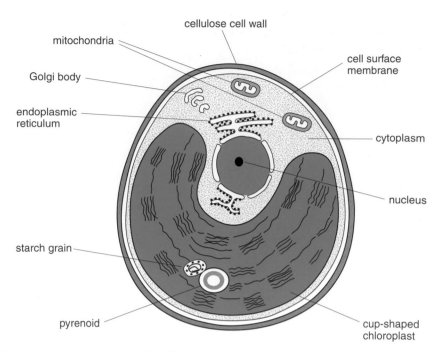

Figure 1.10 The structure of Chlorella

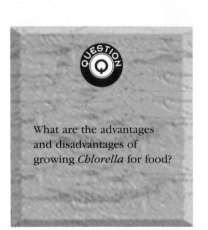

QUESTION

What are the advantages and disadvantages of growing *Chlorella* for food?

Chlorella is of widespread occurrence and can be easily cultured in the laboratory. It was used by Calvin and his co-workers in experiments to determine the sequence of events in the photosynthetic pathway. For more details of these experiments and more information on the process of photosynthesis, reference should be made to the chapter on autotrophic nutrition in *The Organism and the Environment*.

Due to its ease of culture, the high protein content of the cells and its lack of toxicity, it has been suggested that *Chlorella* could be a useful food source for humans and animals. No large-scale production has been carried out as yet. Analysis of the cells has shown that the protein content is about 50% and there are significant quantities of mineral ions and vitamins. It could be used to help in the control of sewage disposal as it has been shown to grow rapidly on raw sewage. As it is photosynthetic, it produces large amounts of oxygen, encouraging the growth of the aerobic bacteria and other organisms responsible for the breakdown of the sewage.

Viruses

Most viruses are less than 0.2 μm in diameter, making an electron microscope necessary to determine their fine structure. They contain a **core** of nucleic acid, either DNA or RNA, often with some protein, surrounded by an outer covering of protein called a **capsid**. There may be an external **envelope**, consisting of a piece of cell surface membrane derived from the previous host cell. In this envelope, some or all of the host cell membrane proteins may be replaced by special viral proteins. There may be exposed glycoproteins on the outside of the envelope, forming **spikes**, which enable the virus to attach to its next host cell.

The functions of the capsids and envelopes are to:

- protect the nucleic acid of the virus from enzymes and chemicals when the virus is outside its host cell
- bind to the surface of the host cell
- assist in the penetration of the host cell and the introduction of the viral nucleic acid.

The capsid is composed of sub-units called **capsomeres**, each consisting of protein molecules. The shape and arrangement of the capsomeres determines whether the virus is classified as:

- **helical**, as in the tobacco mosaic virus (TMV)
- **polyhedral**, as in the herpes virus and the human immunodeficiency virus (HIV)
- **complex**, where there is a polyhedral head and a helical tail as in the λ (lambda) phage.

Helical capsids are composed of rod-shaped capsomeres which bond together, forming a continuous helix, inside which the nucleic acid strand is coiled. Tobacco mosaic virus (TMV) has a helical capsid, with a single strand of RNA coiled inside. The particles of this virus are 15 nm in diameter but can be up to 300 nm in length.

In polyhedral viruses, the capsid is usually a 20-sided polygon with 12 corners, called an **icosahedron**. Two types of capsomeres are involved in its construction: triangular ones form the flat faces of the polygon and round ones form the corners. The nucleic acid is packed into the centre. In the human immunodeficiency virus (HIV), the icosahedral capsid, containing single-stranded RNA, is surrounded by an envelope. HIV is an RNA **retrovirus**. It carries the enzyme **reverse transcriptase**, which can synthesise a single strand of DNA from the viral RNA and then direct the formation of a complementary double strand of DNA. The double-stranded DNA is inserted into a chromosome in the host cell, where it codes for the synthesis of viral proteins.

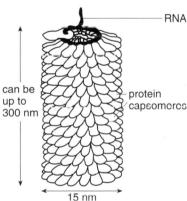

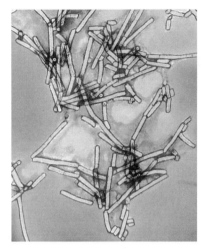

Figure 1.11 (a) Electromnicrograph of tobacco mosaic virus; (b) diagrammatic structure

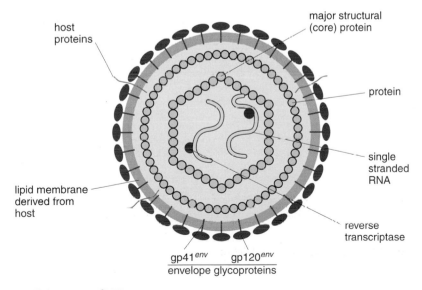

Figure 1.12 Structure of HIV

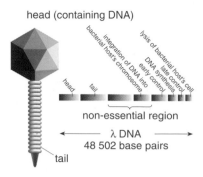

Figure 1.13a Structure of lambda phage

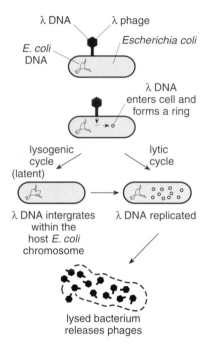

Figure 1.13a Cycle of lambda phage in the bacterium E. coli

The λ (lambda) phage is an example of a bacteriophage, a virus which uses a bacterium as its host. It invades the bacterium *Escherichia coli*, where it can destroy the host cells or insert its DNA into the bacterial chromosome and remain dormant for several generations. The phage consists of a head, containing a double-stranded DNA molecule wrapped around a core of protein surrounded by a polyhedral capsid, and a helical tail.

Microorganisms and disease

An infection is caused when pathogenic microorganisms penetrate the defences of a host organism, enter the tissues and begin to multiply. Damage to the tissues results in a disease. In order to gain entry, it is necessary for the pathogenic organism to bind, or adhere, to its host in some way. It must then penetrate the host's barriers before it can become established in the host's tissues, which, in some cases, are destroyed in the process. In addition, the pathogenic microorganism may produce compounds which are toxic to the host and interfere with the host's metabolic processes.

Amongst bacterial pathogens, structures such as fimbriae, pili, flagella and slime capsules may enable adhesion to the host organism. In viruses, a specific interaction must occur between molecules on the surface of the pathogen and receptors on the host cells. In some cases, the molecules are proteins which form part of the capsid of the virus and in others, the molecules are present in the external envelope. Table 1.5 summarises some of the ways in which bacterial and viral pathogens adhere to their host cells.

Table 1.5 *Ways in which adhesion of bacterial and viral pathogens to host cells is achieved*

Pathogenic microorganism	Disease caused	Means of adhesion
Shigella (bacterium)	dysentery	fimbriae attach to epithelial cells of the intestine
Streptococcus pyogenes (bacterium)	dental caries	slime layer glues the cocci to the tooth surface
poliovirus	poliomyelitis	capsid protein attaches to receptors on cells
human immunodeficiency virus (HIV)	acquired immune deficiency syndrome (AIDS)	spikes of glycoprotein (gp 120) in envelope adhere to CD4 antigen on T-helper cells and monocytes in blood

Many pathogenic microorganisms secrete **exoenzymes** that break down and damage host tissues, thus providing a means of entry. For example, staphylococci can produce the enzyme **hyaluronidase**, which digests hyaluronic acid, the main ground substance causing animal cells to stick together. Fungal plant pathogens may produce **pectinases** which break down the middle lamellae of plant cell walls, allowing entry to the host. Some pathogenic microorganisms secrete poisonous chemical compounds known as **toxins**.

Bacterial pathogens

Both *Salmonella* and *Staphylococcus* produce **enterotoxins**, which are active in the human gut. *Staphylococcus* produces **exotoxins**, which are soluble compounds secreted by the cells into their immediate environment. Only small quantities of such toxins are needed to give rise to symptoms in the host organism. *Salmonella* and other genera of Gram-negative bacteria also produce toxins, but these are not released from the bacteria until the cell wall is damaged or lysis occurs. These toxins are referred to as **endotoxins** and need to be present in large amounts to have any effect, such as causing a fever, inflammation or diarrhoea, in the host. Endotoxins are lipopolysaccharides and form part of the outer membrane of the Gram-negative cell wall.

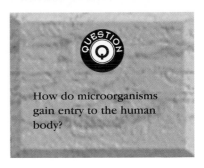

How do microorganisms gain entry to the human body?

Food poisoning can be caused by a number of pathogenic bacteria, but it is interesting to compare the onset of symptoms due to *Staphylococcus aureus* with that of *Salmonella enteriditis*. With *Staphylococcus*, the onset of vomiting and diarrhoea occurs from 1 to 6 hours after the ingestion of the exotoxin in foods such as cream, cooked meats and poultry. With *Salmonella*, the onset of diarrhoea does not occur until 1 or 2 days after eating infected eggs or undercooked poultry. In this case, the bacteria from the infected food stick to the surface of epithelial cells lining the intestine. The bacteria are taken up into the cells by phagocytosis. Cell damage occurs when the bacteria multiply and produce endotoxins, which cause fever and inflammation of the tissue.

Mycobacterium tuberculosis is the organism responsible for the disease **tuberculosis** in humans. The spread of the disease is due to the inhalation of the organism into the respiratory tract. When the bacteria reach the alveoli of the lungs, they are engulfed by macrophages. The bacteria are able to survive and multiply within the macrophages. Other macrophages are attracted to the site of infection, ingest the bacteria and then carry the bacteria to lymph nodes, where a cell-mediated immune response is stimulated. T-cells become sensitised and produce lymphokines which activate macrophages to destroy the bacteria. The body reacts to the invasion by forming 'tubercles', which are small granular nodules, around the bacteria, thus isolating them. The bacteria do no direct damage to the tissues and there is no damage due to toxins. Primary infections due to these bacteria are usually mild and go no further, but secondary infections, due to the activation of dormant bacteria, may occur in about 10 per cent of cases. If the bacteria are not contained within the tubercles, they may invade the bloodstream and spread to other areas of the body. An affected person may show fatigue, weight loss, weakness and fever. If the infection occurs in the lungs, there is a characteristic, chronic cough with blood-stained sputum. Tissue destruction occurs in the lungs and blood vessels can rupture causing haemorrhage.

The cell wall of *Mycobacterium* contains peptidoglycans and stains Gram positive, but it also contains lipids, giving it a thick waxy outer coat which is highly resistant to chemicals and dyes. This waxy outer coat prevents desiccation and enables the bacteria to survive for long periods of time in the air and in house dust. Infected people cough up large numbers of the bacteria, so strict measures have to be taken to prevent the spread of infection.

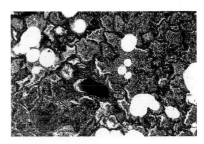

Figure 1.14 Light micrograph of human lung affected by tuberculosis

Fungal pathogens

Fungi can cause diseases in both plants and animals. The most common fungal diseases in humans are those which affect the skin and mucus membranes, but fungal spores can enter via the respiratory tract and cause lung diseases. Fungal infections in plants are also common and are of significant importance. Diseases such as potato blight and the rusts and mildews affecting cereals can reduce crop yields drastically.

Figure 1.15 Oral thrush, caused by the yeast-like fungus Candida albicans

Candida albicans is a yeast-like fungus, commonly present in the mouth and gut of humans. Normally it is a harmless component of the population of microorganisms which can exist on and within the body, causing no symptoms. If conditions change and the normal resistance of the body alters, the fungus can multiply and cause the condition known as **thrush**, or **candidiasis**. Oral thrush is common in small babies, but it can also affect elderly people and those who are immune-suppressed, such as sufferers from AIDS. Babies are thought to become infected during birth from organisms present in the mother's vagina. As the new-born infant has no resident population of microorganisms, the fungus grows and multiplies, producing fluffy, white patches in the mouth. If these patches are lifted up, the surface epithelium underneath is red due to the penetration of the hyphae. The fungus causes soreness and if not treated, may lead to secondary infection by bacteria.

The fungus can infect other areas of the body, including the gut, lungs and vagina. *Candida* is normally present in the vagina, but it does not cause problems because its growth is inhibited by the acid pH, usually between pH 4 and pH 5, and competition from other microorganisms. Circumstances which cause the pH of the vaginal secretions to change and become more alkaline, may favour the growth of the fungus. This can cause itching, burning sensations and a discharge to occur, giving rise to the condition known as vaginal thrush. Changes in the pH may be caused by menstruation, pregnancy, taking oral contraceptives or diabetes. In addition, prolonged use of anti-inflammatory drugs or a course of a broad-spectrum antibiotic may upset the balance of the microorganisms in the vagina, removing competition and allowing the fungus to flourish, resulting in the same symptoms. Control measures include:

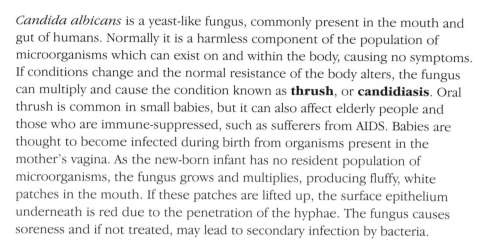

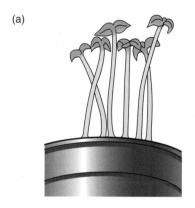

(a)

(b)

- application of gentian violet paint to infected areas
- the use of an anti-fungal compound, such as Nystatin, in lotions, creams or lozenges
- reduction in the pH of the vagina by treatment with natural yoghurt: this will reduce the pH and introduce live bacteria which compete with the fungus.

Figure 1.16 Damping off disease in seedlings of Pythium debaryanum: (top) normal seedlings; (bottom) seedlings showing damping off.

Pythium debaryanum is a fungal plant pathogen which causes **damping-off disease in Crucifers** (cabbage family). The fungus is a **facultative parasite**: it can exist as a saprobiont in the soil, but can infect young seedlings, destroy the tissues and then feed on the dead remains.

Pythium belongs to the phylum Zygomycota. The mycelium is coenocytic, with no cross walls, and reproduces asexually by means of spores and sexually by the formation of oospores. Infection of seedlings can occur from spores or mycelia in the soil, or from neighbouring infected plants. The hyphae can enter the seedlings through the stomata or penetrate the epidermis by secreting pectinases which break down the middle lamellae of the cell walls. Once inside the host's tissues, the hyphae grow intercellularly, sending branches into cells and absorbing nutrients. About five days after infection, the seedlings fall over due to the destruction of the tissues of the hypocotyl region of the stem at soil level. Asexual reproduction can occur very quickly after infection and masses of spores are produced, causing rapid spread of the disease, particularly in the humid conditions found in glasshouses.

Control measures are difficult, as the fungus can survive for long periods in soil and can also spread very rapidly when conditions are favourable. Soil sterilisation by steam or chemicals is often used for glasshouse crops. Susceptible crops should be grown in well-drained soils and the overcrowding of seedlings should be avoided.

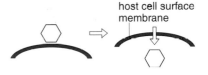

Damping-off disease may be controlled by the use of a fungicide. What are the advantages and disadvantages of the use of fungicides?

Viral pathogens

All viruses are parasitic, so must enter the cells of a living organism in order to reproduce. As parasites, they are usually pathogenic, causing symptoms in the host organisms. As virus particles are incapable of independent movement, they have to be transmitted between hosts in some way. The commonest forms of transmission of viruses affecting humans are by:
- droplet inhalation
- contaminated food or water
- insect bites
- sexual transmission.

Plant viruses may be transmitted by insect vectors or gain entry to plants by mechanical means, such as physical damage during cultivation.

Viruses show **host specificity**, usually infecting only a restricted range of host species. Once inside the host organism, the virus particles attach to specific host cells by means of interactions between molecules on the capsid or the envelope and receptor molecules in the host cell membrane. Once attachment has been achieved, the virus can enter the host cell in one of three ways:
- by direct translocation across the cell surface membrane
- by fusion of the viral and cell surface membranes
- by uptake into a special vesicle or phagosome.

Once inside the host cell, the capsid is shed and the viral nucleic acid is released. Viral messenger RNA is formed and the host cell's ribosomes are used to synthesise viral protein molecules for the formation of new capsids. In addition, new viral nucleic acid is replicated, usually in the nucleus of the host cell. New virus particles are assembled, with the capsids forming around the nucleic acid. This process may take place in the cytoplasm or the nucleus of the host cell.

(a) Direct translocation across cell membrane

host cell surface membrane

(b) Fusion of viral and cell membranes

viral envelope

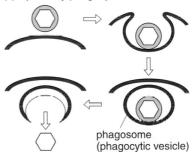

(c) Uptake by phagocytosis

phagosome (phagocytic vesicle)

Figure 1.17 Methods of entry into host cells shown by viruses

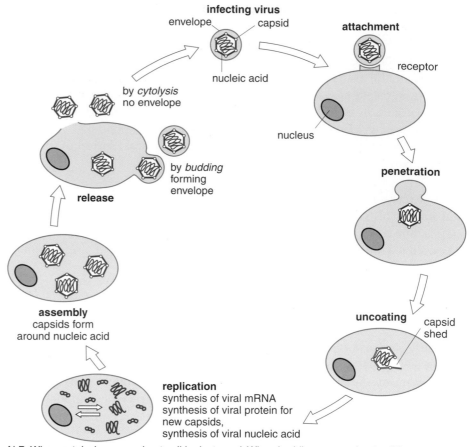

infecting virus

envelope   capsid

nucleic acid

attachment

receptor

nucleus

penetration

uncoating

capsid shed

replication
synthesis of viral mRNA
synthesis of viral protein for
new capsids,
synthesis of viral nucleic acid

assembly
capsids form
around nucleic acid

release

by *cytolysis*
no envelope

by *budding*
forming
envelope

N.B. When cytolysis occurs, host cell is destroyed. When budding occurs, host cell is not
     destroyed and may go on producing virus particles for some time.

Figure 1.18 Cycle of infection and replication

In viruses that lack envelopes, lysis of the host cell results in the release of the new virus particles. It is of relevance to note that the host cell is destroyed in this process. The cycle of infection, replication and release by lysis is referred to as a **lytic cycle** and results in a **lytic infection**.

In viruses with envelopes, viral envelope proteins and glycoproteins are inserted into specific areas of the host cell surface membrane. The new virus particles are attracted to these regions and the host membrane becomes extended forming buds around the virus particles. The buds become pinched off, and each virus particle is now surrounded by a modified portion of the host cell surface membrane containing viral proteins and glycoproteins. In this process, the host cell is not destroyed, so infected cells can bud off new virus particles for long periods, often at a slow rate, giving rise to a **persistent infection**. This type of infection is characteristic of diseases such as hepatitis B, where an infected person may act as a symptomless carrier capable of passing the condition on to other people.

In **latent infections**, the viral genetic material may become incorporated in the genome of the host cell, as in the retroviruses and bacteriophage, or it may remain in the cytoplasm, as in herpes. Replication does not take place until some signal, such as stress or cell damage, triggers a release from latency.

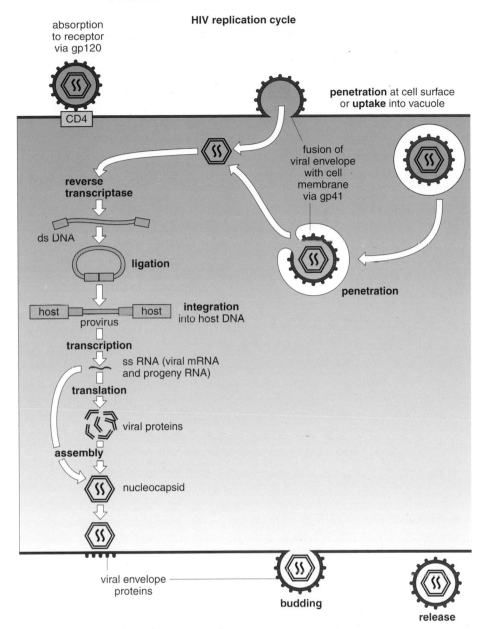

Figure 1.19 Envelope formation as part of the HIV replication cycle

The human immunodeficiency virus (HIV) has an envelope containing glycoproteins, designated gp41 and gp120. As the virus enters the bloodstream, it infects T-helper cells (otherwise known as T4 lymphocytes or T4 cells), monocytes and macrophages, which have a surface protein CD4. This protein molecule acts as a binding site for the viral glycoprotein gp120. The virus particles are then either taken into the cells in vesicles formed by the T4 cell membrane or enter by fusion with the membrane. Once inside the cells, the genetic material of the virus, in the form of single-stranded RNA, is converted into double-stranded DNA and incorporated into the genome of the host cell. Replication of the virus and cell destruction does not occur straight away as infected T4 cells need to be activated, so the virus is said to be **latent**. Activation of infected T4 cells may be triggered as a result of a secondary infection.

THE RANGE OF MICROORGANISMS: MICROORGANISMS AND DISEASE

What are the advantages of offering an HIV test to all pregnant women?

There is a poor response by the immune system of the body to infection by HIV. Some antibodies may be produced, but these fail to eliminate the infection, so the virus persists. There are functional changes in affected cells, together with some destruction of T4 cells, leading to a depressed immune response generally and an increased liability to secondary infections by other microorganisms. Gradually the number of T4 cells decreases, there is an increase in replication of the virus and the secondary infections become more difficult to control. Eventually the infected person may develop AIDS (acquired immune deficiency syndrome). The lymph glands become enlarged and more malignant conditions, such as Kaposi's sarcoma, develop with inevitably fatal results.

Within an individual, the virus spreads by cell-to-cell transmission as a result of the fusion of infected cells with uninfected ones and infected cells can pass from one body system to another. Transmission from person to person can occur via infected blood or by sexual intercourse. Babies of HIV positive mothers can become infected before birth by transmission of the virus across the placenta or after birth through breast-feeding.

Some drugs, such as AZT, have been shown to prolong survival and quality of life in AIDS sufferers, but at present, there is no known cure. Much research is being carried out to develop a vaccine and to identify vulnerable stages in the infection and replication cycle of the virus. The best available methods of prevention and control are the education and counselling of the public in the avoidance of transmission of the virus.

Tobacco mosaic virus (TMV) is a viral pathogen which causes irregular mottled patches to appear on the leaves of tobacco and other plants. The patches may be light and dark green or yellowish-brown in colour and indicate areas where cells and tissues have been killed by the virus. The virus enters the plant via the stomata or by cuts on the leaves. Its usual means of transmission is by workers handling the plants during the cultivation of the crop. No specific insect vector has been identified and it is thought unlikely that aphids are involved in the transmission.

Tobacco mosaic virus is one of the most persistent plant viruses known and because it is transmitted mechanically, it is very difficult to control. Much cured tobacco contains viral particles, so workers who smoke and then handle plants in the field can transmit the disease. The virus can affect a wide range of other plants, including tomatoes, and there are many different strains. It persists in soil and can enter the roots of plants if there are damaged areas, but it is thought that there is not much infection carried over through the seeds. The effect of the virus on the production of the crop is difficult to assess, but leaf growth is restricted. In other virus diseases of crop plants, such as sugar beet yellows, infected leaves will affect the photosynthetic processes, resulting in a smaller crop. Control measures include:
- avoidance of growing susceptible crops in soil known to be contaminated
- sterilisation of soil used for seedbeds
- hygienic handling of crops by workers
- use of resistant varieties of crops.

Culture techniques

Requirements for growth

Like all living organisms, microorganisms require an energy source, usually in the form of an organic carbon compound, and a range of other nutrients for metabolism and cell growth. Microorganisms can be divided into two main groups according to the source of energy utilised. **Phototrophs** use light as an energy source, whereas **chemotrophs** use different chemical substances as their source of energy. Many microorganisms use organic substances as energy sources, although some are able to use inorganic substances. These are both different types of chemotrophs, but those which use organic substances as energy sources are known as **chemoorganotrophs**, whereas those which use inorganic substances are referred to as **chemolithotrophs**.

The nutrients which are required by microorganisms can be divided into two groups:
- **macronutrients**, which are required in relatively large amounts
- **micronutrients**, which are required in small quantities.

Macronutrients include carbon, hydrogen, oxygen, nitrogen, sulphur, magnesium and iron (Table 2.1). All nutrients have to be provided in a suitable form in the culture media in which the microorganisms are grown. Carbon is often provided in the form of organic substances, including glucose, organic acids, fatty acids or amino acids. Phototrophic microorganisms, such as *Chlorella*, use carbon dioxide as their carbon source. Nitrogen is available to microorganisms either in organic substances, such as amino acids or nucleotide bases, or as inorganic substances including ammonia or nitrate ions. Many bacteria are able to use ammonia as their only source of nitrogen; the nitrogen fixing bacteria, such as *Rhizobium*, use nitrogen gas.

Table 2.1 *Macronutrients required by microorganisms and the forms in which they are supplied in culture media*

Elements	Forms in which the elements are supplied in culture media
carbon (C)	glucose, organic acids, yeast extract, peptone
hydrogen (H)	water, organic compounds
oxygen (O)	water, oxygen gas, organic compounds
nitrogen (N)	nitrogen gas, ammonium ions, nitrate ions, amino acids, nucleotide bases
phosphorus (P)	inorganic phosphates
sulphur (S)	sulphates, sulphur-containing amino acids
magnesium (Mg)	magnesium salts such as magnesium sulphate
sodium (Na)	sodium chloride
calcium (Ca)	calcium chloride
iron (Fe)	iron salts such as iron sulphate
potassium (K)	potassium salts such as potassium chloride

Micronutrients (or trace elements) are metals and are essential for normal cell function. They are required in very small quantities and it is not normally necessary to add these separately to culture media as they will often be present in sufficient quantities in other ingredients. Micronutrients include copper, manganese, vanadium and zinc. These may function as enzyme activators or as constituents of enzyme molecules. Iron is sometimes considered to be a micronutrient, although it is required in larger quantities than the other metals.

In addition to these micronutrients, microorganisms may also require certain organic growth factors in very small amounts. Such factors include amino acids, vitamins, purines and pyrimidines. These compounds can be synthesised by the majority of microorganisms, but some microorganisms may require one or more of these to be present in their culture media.

All the nutrients required by microorganisms must be provided in the media in which they are grown. There are two main types of culture media used in microbiology, **defined** and **undefined** (or complex) media. Defined media are made up using pure chemical substances, dissolved in distilled water so that the exact chemical composition is known. Undefined media contain mixtures of substances such as yeast extract, peptone, or casein hydrolysate, in which the exact composition is unknown. To illustrate these types of culture media, Table 2.2 shows examples of culture media for *Escherichia coli*.

Table 2.2 *Examples of culture media for* E. coli

Defined culture medium for *Escherichia coli*		Undefined culture medium for *E. coli*	
K_2HPO_4	7 g	glucose	15 g
KH_2PO_4	2 g	yeast extract	5 g
$(NH_4)_2SO_4$	1 g	peptone	5 g
$MgSO_4$	0.1 g	KH_2PO_4	2 g
$CaCl_2$	0.02 g	distilled water	1 dm^3
glucose	4 to 10 g		
micronutrients (Fe, Co, Mn, Zn, Cu, Ni, Mo)	2 to 10 μg each		
distilled water	1 dm^3		

Environmental influences on growth

We have described the nutrients which are required by microorganisms for growth, but there are several other factors which have important influences on growth. These factors include temperature, availability of oxygen, light (for phototrophic microorganisms) and pH. Temperature is one of the most important factors. In general, as temperature increases, enzyme activity within the cells also increases and growth becomes faster. However, above a certain temperature, proteins – including enzymes – will be denatured. Therefore, growth will increase up to a point above which enzymes become denatured and inactivated. Above this point, growth rate falls rapidly to zero. For every

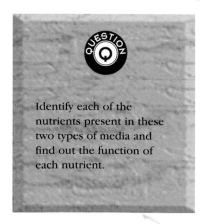

Identify each of the nutrients present in these two types of media and find out the function of each nutrient.

microorganism, there is a minimum temperature, below which there is no growth, an optimum temperature where growth occurs at the most rapid rate and a maximum temperature above which growth will not occur.

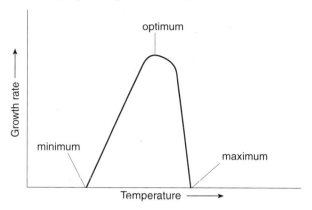

Figure 2.1 The effect of temperature on the growth rate of a microorganism

The optimum temperature for microorganisms varies widely; some have optima between 5 and 10 °C, whereas at the other extreme, some have optima at 80 °C or above. Microorganisms can be divided into four groups on the basis of their temperature optima:

- **psychrophiles**, which have low optima, e.g. *Flavobacterium*, optimum 13 °C
- **mesophiles**, which have mid-range optima, e.g. *Escherichia coli*, optimum 39 °C
- **thermophiles**, with high optima, e.g. *Bacillus stearothermophilus*, optimum 60 °C
- **hyperthermophiles**, with very high optima, e.g. *Thermococcus celer*, optimum 88 °C.

Microorganisms also vary in their requirements for oxygen. Some grow only in the presence of oxygen, whereas others grow only in the absence of oxygen. To the latter group of microorganisms, oxygen is actually toxic, probably because they are unable to remove toxic products of oxygen metabolism, such as hydrogen peroxide. On the basis of their requirements for oxygen, microorganisms can be separated into several groups, as outlined below:

- **obligate aerobes**, which will grow only in the presence of oxygen, e.g. *Micrococcus luteus*
- **facultative aerobes**, which can grow in the absence of oxygen, but grow better if oxygen is supplied, e.g. *Escherichia coli*
- **microaerophilic aerobes**, which require oxygen at lower concentrations than atmospheric, e.g. *Spirillum volutans*
- **obligate anaerobes**, which will grow only in the absence of oxygen, e.g. *Desulphovibrio*.

In small-scale culture, such as on agar in Petri dishes or in universal containers of broth media, oxygen diffuses directly from the air to the microorganisms. However, if aerobic microorganisms are grown on a larger scale, such as in a laboratory fermenter, it is necessary to aerate the culture, usually by bubbling sterile air through the medium. This supplies the microorganisms with oxygen,

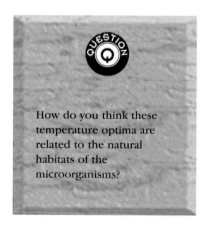

How do you think these temperature optima are related to the natural habitats of the microorganisms?

CULTURE TECHNIQUES

Figure 2.2 An anaerobic jar for the incubation of cultures under anaerobic conditions. Air in the jar is replaced with an oxygen-free gas mixture, such as hydrogen and carbon dioxide, or a chemical catalyst is placed in the jar which removes oxygen from the atmosphere

where otherwise the rate of diffusion and poor solubility of oxygen in water would mean that insufficient oxygen was available. If it is necessary to culture obligate anaerobes, for example in a hospital laboratory, they are grown on agar plates placed in a special container referred to as an **anaerobic jar**, a container which can be filled with a mixture of hydrogen and carbon dioxide to replace the air. The jar contains a catalyst which will remove any residual oxygen, to ensure anaerobic conditions.

We have seen that microorganisms vary widely in their tolerance to environmental temperatures and availability of oxygen; they also have a wide range of environmental pH values at which they can grow. Most microorganisms have a pH optimum between 5 and 9, but a few species can grow at pH values outside this range. In general, fungi tend to be more tolerant of acid conditions than bacteria, with optima at pH 5 or below. These pH values refer to the extracellular environment, and although this may vary widely, the intracellular pH remains nearly neutral. The pH of culture media is kept relatively constant by the use of buffer solutions, such as phosphate buffers. During the growth of a microorganism, the pH of the medium may change due to the production of acidic or alkaline products of metabolism and this may be regulated by the addition of appropriate sterile buffer solutions during the growth phase.

Growth of cultures

Under favourable conditions, the number of single-celled microorganisms will double at regular intervals. This is because each of the two daughter cells produced will have the same potential for growth as the original parental cell. The time required for the number of cells to double is known as the mean doubling time. Table 2.3 shows how the number of cells will increase, starting with a single cell, assuming a doubling time of 20 minutes. The table shows both the arithmetic number of cells, and the number expressed as a logarithm to the base 10.

Table 2.3 *Increases in the numbers of bacterial cells with a doubling time of 20 minutes*

Time / minutes	Number of divisions	Number of cells	Log_{10} number of cells
0	0	1	0.000
20	1	2	0.301
40	2	4	0.602
60	3	8	0.903
80	4	16	1.204
100	5	32	1.505
120	6	64	1.806
140	7	128	2.107
160	8	256	2.408
180	9	512	2.709
200	10	1024	3.010

A graph showing the log number of cells plotted against time is a straight line, as long as the cells are dividing at a steady rate. If N_0 is the size of the population at a certain time, and N_t is the size at a later time, t, then the number of generations which has occurred can be calculated using the following formula:

$$N_t = 2^{kt} \times N_0$$

where k is the exponential growth rate constant, that is, the number of doublings per unit time, usually expressed as the number of doublings per hour.

The exponential growth rate constant, k, can be found using the formula:

$$k = \frac{\log_2 N_t - \log_2 N_0}{t}$$

where $\log_2 N_0$ is the log to the base 2 of the initial population size, and $\log_2 N_t$ is the log to the base 2 of the final population size, after t hours.

Rather than using logarithms to the base 2, the calculation can be made using logarithms of N_0 and N_t to the base 10, and dividing by $\log_{10} 2$, which can be taken as 0.301:

$$k = \frac{\log_{10} N_t - \log_{10} N_0}{0.301 \times t}$$

Let us consider a specific example. Suppose that the number of bacteria in a population increases from 10^2 cells to 10^9 cells in 8 hours. The exponential growth rate can be calculated as follows.

$$k = \frac{\log_{10} 10^9 - \log_{10} 10^2}{0.301 \times 8}$$

$$= \frac{9 - 2}{2.408}$$

$$= 2.91 \text{ generations per hour}$$

The growth rate is sometimes expressed as the time taken for the population to double, or the **mean doubling time**. This is the reciprocal of the exponential growth rate, that is, 1/k. In the example above, then mean doubling time is 1/2.91, or approximately 21 minutes.

So far, we have considered cells only in the exponential phase of growth. Cell growth, with a limited supply of nutrients, does not continue indefinitely. The growth of the population is normally limited by either the exhaustion of one or more essential nutrients, or by the accumulation of toxic by-products of metabolism. Figure 2.3 shows a complete growth curve for a microorganism. Four distinct phases of growth can be seen:
- lag phase
- exponential (or logarithmic) phase
- stationary phase
- death phase.

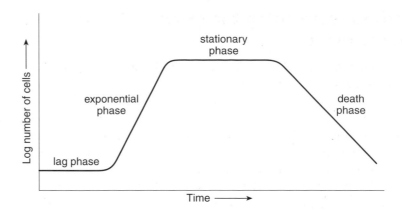

Figure 2.3 Typical growth curve for a bacterial culture

When fresh, sterile medium is inoculated with a culture of a microorganism, growth may not begin immediately. There is a period of time in which the cells are synthesising the enzymes required for the metabolism of nutrients present in the medium. This period of time is referred to as the **lag phase**, and can be seen as a period of adjustment to the culture conditions. A lag phase does not always occur. If, for example, cells which were already in the exponential phase were transferred to fresh, identical medium, exponential growth would continue at the same rate.

We have already described the **exponential phase** as a period of constant growth in the size of the microbial population, in which both cell numbers and cell mass increase in parallel. The growth rate constant is affected by both genetic and environmental factors; it varies from one species to another, and is influenced by such factors as the concentration of nutrients in the growth medium, temperature and pH. The exponential phase is followed by the **stationary phase**, in which the overall growth rate is zero. During this phase, slow growth of some cells may occur, which is balanced by the death of others, so that the total number of viable cells remains constant. This phase is followed by the **death phase** in which the number of viable cells progressively decreases. Death of cells may be accompanied by cell lysis so that both the total cell number and the viable cell count decreases.

Diauxic growth is sometimes observed if a microorganism is grown in a medium containing two different carbon sources. Diauxic growth is characterised by two distinct phases of exponential growth, separated by a brief lag phase. For example, if *Escherichia coli* is grown in a medium containing both glucose and lactose, the glucose will be metabolised first. Glucose actually inhibits the synthesis of lactase (β-galactosidase) (referred to as catabolite repression) and only after the glucose has been used up will lactase be synthesised. Growth then resumes using lactose as an energy source.

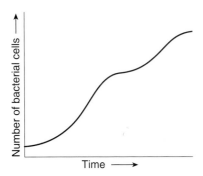

Figure 2.4 Diauxic growth of E. coli *in a medium containing glucose and lactose*

Methods for measuring the growth of microorganisms

We have seen that the growth of a culture of unicellular microorganisms results from an increase in the number of cells, so growth of microbial populations can be measured by determining changes in either the number of cells, or the cell mass. The number of cells in a suspension can be determined by counting the number of cells present in an accurately determined, very small volume of culture medium. This is usually carried out using special microscope slides, known as **counting chambers** (see Practical: *Counting cells using a haemocytometer*). These are slides which are ruled with a grid of squares of known area and are made so that when correctly filled, they contain a film of liquid of known depth. The volume of liquid overlying each square is therefore known. This method for determining cell numbers is referred to as a **total cell count**, which includes both viable and non-viable cells, as it is not normally possible to distinguish one from another using a microscope.

The number of cells can also be determined using a **plate count** (see Practical: *Counting cells using the pour plate dilution method*). This method depends on the ability of each single, viable cell to grow in or on an agar medium and produce a visible colony. This method of counting is referred to as a **viable count**, as only those cells which are able to grow in the culture medium are detected. Appropriate dilutions of a bacterial culture are made and are used to inoculate a suitable medium. The number of viable cells present in the original culture is then determined by counting the number of colonies which develop after incubation of the plates, and multiplying this number by the dilution factor. Two or three replicate plates of each dilution should be prepared, to reduce the sampling error. The greatest accuracy is obtained with relatively large numbers of colonies on each plate, but the practical limit is reached with between 300 and 400 colonies per plate.

The only direct method for determining **cell mass** is to measure the dry mass of cells in a known volume of culture medium. This is a suitable method for measuring the growth of a filamentous organism, where cell counting is inappropriate, but it is rarely used for unicellular bacteria because of the relatively insensitive method for weighing. It is difficult to weigh with an accuracy of less than 1 mg, but this represents the dry mass of between 1 and 5×10^9 bacteria.

One useful approach for estimating the number of cells present in a suspension is to use an **optical method**, by determining the amount of light which is scattered by a cell suspension. A suspension of cells appears cloudy, or turbid, to the eye because the cells scatter light passing through the suspension. The cloudiness increases as the cell numbers increase and, within limits, the amount of light scattered by the cells is proportional to their numbers. A **colorimeter** is an instrument which can be used to measure the amount of light which is transmitted by a cell suspension. When a beam of light passes through a cell suspension, the reduction in the amount of light transmitted gives a measure of cell density. A colorimeter can be calibrated, by combining measurements of light transmitted with another method for measuring cell growth, such as plate counting.

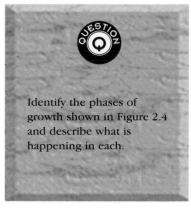

QUESTION

Identify the phases of growth shown in Figure 2.4 and describe what is happening in each.

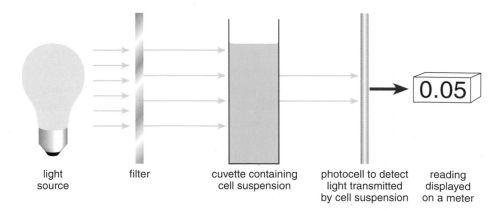

Figure 2.5 Principle of a colorimeter used to measure cell growth

Sterilisation is the removal or killing of ALL microorganisms on an object or in any material. After sterilisation, microorganisms will not be able to grow even under the most favourable conditions.

Methods for culturing microorganisms

If we wish to study a single species of microorganism, it is often necessary to isolate it from a mixed culture of many different species. Microorganisms are present in almost every habitat, soil and water are particularly rich sources, and in order to obtain a pure culture of a single species, it must be grown in a laboratory in suitable conditions, with all the necessary nutrients provided. It is also essential to avoid contaminating the culture with other, unwanted microorganisms. The medium used to grow the microorganism must be sterile, and it is essential to take precautions in handling the materials used for culture of the organism in order to avoid contamination.

Aseptic technique is the term used describe the proper handling of cultures, sterile apparatus and sterile media to prevent contamination. The method used to pour sterile agar medium into Petri dishes is described on page 72. Transfer of cultures from a mixed broth culture onto an agar plate, is usually carried out using a bacteriological loop which has been sterilised by heating until it is red hot using a Bunsen burner. If we wish to isolate a fungus from a mouldy tomato, a mounted needle can be used, sterilised in the same way as the loop. The needle is then used to transfer some of the fungal material, including spores, from the tomato to the centre of a Petri dish containing a suitable medium, such as malt extract agar.

Microbiological media are formulated to contain all the nutrients required by particular microorganisms. Some species of microorganism are particularly fastidious in their requirements and their media are therefore complex, containing a wide range of mineral salts, amino acids, purines, pyrimidines, vitamins and other organic growth factors. Other microorganisms will grow in relatively simple media containing an energy source, usually glucose, and a number of mineral salts. Different microorganisms therefore have different nutrient requirements and for the successful culture of a particular species it is necessary to provide all the essential nutrients, in the correct proportions, in the culture media.

Selective media contain substances which selectively inhibit the growth of certain microorganisms, whilst allowing others to grow. These media are

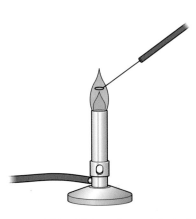

Figure 2.6 Sterilising a bacteriological loop. The loop should be held in the flame until it is red hot, then allowed to cool briefly before being used to transfer a culture aseptically. The loop must always be flamed again after use

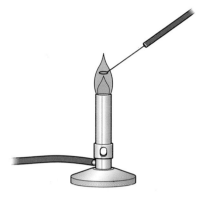

1 Flame the loop until red hot then allow to cool in the air

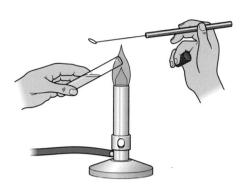

2 If you are right-handed, hold the loop as shown and remove the cap from the tube with the third and fourth fingers of your right hand. Flame the neck of the tube by passing through the Bunsen flame.

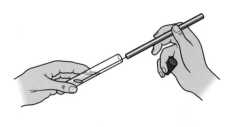

3 Use the cooled loop to remove a sample of the culture

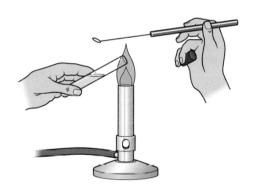

4 Hold the loop still and remove the tube. Flame the neck of the tube again and replace the cap carefully.

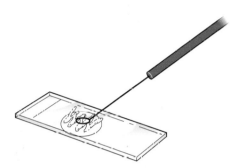

5 Use the loop to prepare a smear on a slide, to inoculate another tube or prepare a streak plate.

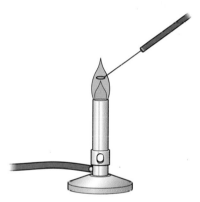

6 Flame the loop again to sterilise it after use.

Figure 2.7 Using a bacteriological loop to carry out an aseptic transfer

particularly important in medical microbiology, as they are used to culture and isolate organisms from clinical specimens such as blood and urine. An example of a selective medium is MacConkey agar, which contains lactose and bile salts. This is used to isolate enteric bacteria, that is, bacteria which grow in the intestinal tract. Bacteria such as *Escherichia coli*, which are able to utilise lactose as an energy source, are able to grow, but the growth of other species of bacteria, including *Staphylococcus* spp. will be inhibited.

Some microbiological media contain a coloured pH indicator substance, such as phenol red or bromocresol purple. These are known as **indicator media** (or differential media) and will show whether or not a change in pH has occurred as a result of the metabolism of the bacteria during growth. For example, if the bacteria produce acids, then a broth medium containing phenol red will change in colour from red to yellow. Eosin methylene blue (EMB) agar is an example of a medium which is both selective and an indicator medium and is used to isolate Gram-negative enteric bacteria. EMB agar contains lactose and sucrose as energy sources, and the dyes eosin and methylene blue. Methylene blue inhibits the growth of Gram-positive bacteria; eosin changes colour according to the pH of the medium, changing from colourless to black in acidic conditions. *E. coli* will grow in EMB agar to produce colonies which are black, with a greenish metallic sheen. *Salmonella* produces colonies which are translucent, or pink.

Although selective media are important in the isolation and identification of bacteria, many species can be successfully cultivated using nutrient broth, or nutrient agar. The composition of nutrient broth is given on page 70. Broth media may be solidified by the addition of **agar**, a polysaccharide obtained from red algae. Agar is usually added at about 1.5 per cent by weight to the medium, and dissolved by boiling. On cooling to about 42 °C, the medium will set to produce a clear, firm gel.

Find out why agar is used as a setting agent for microbiological media in preference to gelatine.

Use of fermenters

Microorganisms may be grown on a large scale for the purposes of producing a wide range of useful products including antibiotics, enzymes, food additives and ethanol. This exploitation of microorganisms is described in detail in Chapter 3, with particular reference to the production of enzymes, mycoprotein, and medical applications.

Fermenters are vessels used for the growth of microorganisms in liquid media. These vary in size from small scale laboratory fermenters containing perhaps 250 cm^3 of medium, to very large scale industrial fermenters containing up to 500 000 dm^3. The majority of microorganisms grown are aerobic and it is therefore essential to ensure an adequate supply of oxygen to maintain aerobic conditions.

Two main systems for culturing microorganisms are used, referred to as **batch culture** and **continuous culture**. In batch culture, growth of the microorganism occurs in a fixed volume of medium and, apart from oxygen, substances are not normally added to the medium during culture. The organism typically goes through the usual phases of growth, that is, lag, exponential and stationary. The organism continues to grow in the medium until conditions become unfavourable. In continuous culture, fresh, sterile medium is added to the fermenter at a constant rate and spent medium, together with cells, is removed at the same rate. The number of cells and the composition of the medium in the fermenter therefore remains constant. Continuous culture can, theoretically, run indefinitely but, apart from the production of Quorn™ mycoprotein, few industrial cultures are maintained continuously.

To illustrate the principle of a fermenter, Figure 2.8 shows a simple fermenter which is suitable for use in a school laboratory.

This fermenter could be used to grow an organism such as yeast (*Saccharomyces cerevisiae*) under controlled conditions. Before use, the syringes are removed and suitable broth medium added to the flask. The ends of the tubes are then covered with aluminium foil and the whole apparatus is sterilised by autoclaving. When in use, the fermenter may be kept at a constant temperature by standing it in a water bath at, say, 30 °C. Filter-sterilised air is supplied by means of an aquarium pump, and waste gases are vented through another filter. The small syringe at the top of the apparatus is used to inoculate the sterile medium with a culture of the organism to be grown and samples may be removed at regular intervals using the syringe at the side. In this way, the growth of the organism may be monitored using a suitable counting technique, such as a haemocytometer, or by the pour plate dilution method. These are described in the Practical section, pages 76 to 79. This apparatus could also be used for growing *Chlorella* in a mineral salts medium and keeping the fermenter illuminated using, for example, a Gro-lux fluorescent tube.

Figure 2.9 shows an industrial fermenter to illustrate how the simple fermenter is scaled up.

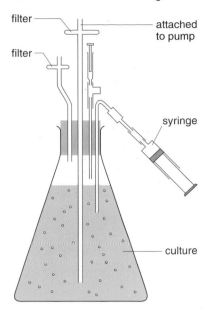

Figure 2.8 A simple fermenter

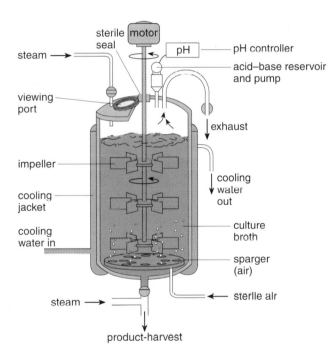

Figure 2.9 Diagram of an industrial fermenter, such as that used to produce the antibiotic penicillin

Industrial fermenters are usually made of stainless steel, which can be sterilised by passing steam, under pressure, through the whole equipment. Industrial fermenters have a number of important features including:

- a **cooling jacket** through which cold water is passed to remove excess heat produced by metabolic activities of the microorganisms. If the culture is not cooled in this way, the temperature would increase to a point at which enzymes would start to be denatured and the microorganisms killed.

- an efficient system for the **aeration** of the culture. This includes a **sparger** a device through which sterile air is pumped under a high pressure, breaking the stream of air into fine bubbles. An **impeller** is used to stir the contents of the fermenter. Stirring mixes air bubbles with the medium, helping oxygen to dissolve and ensures the microorganisms are kept mixed with the medium. This ensures that access to nutrients is maintained.

- systems for monitoring the growth of the culture, controlling the pH by the addition of buffers, and for removing the products when growth is completed.

To illustrate the principle of an industrial fermenter, the production of the antibiotic penicillin can be used. The discovery of penicillin is described in chapter 3, page 56. Fleming's original isolate was a strain of *Penicillium notatum*, which yielded about 20 units of penicillin per cm^3 when grown on the surface of a broth medium (1 million units of penicillin G = 0.6 g). A search for natural variants of *Penicillium* led to the isolation of *P. chrysogenum*, strain NRRL 1951, from a mouldy melon purchased at a market in Peoria, USA. The introduction of this strain, together with a change in culture methods, increased the yield of penicillin to 100 units per cm^3. Repeated steps of mutation and selection have led to the development of the strains of *P. chrysogenum* used today, which produce penicillin at a concentration of about 30 000 units per cm^3. Industrially, *P. chrysogenum* is grown in large fermenters (with a capacity of up to 200 000 dm^3) similar to that shown in Figure 2.9. The fungus is grown initially in the laboratory on a small scale to produce an inoculum, which is used ultimately to inoculate the fermenter. *P. chrysogenum* is grown in stages, from a solid medium, to flask culture in a broth medium, through to 'seed stages' of up to 100 m^3 in order to obtain a large enough inoculum to ensure rapid growth in the final fermenter. Many media for the production of penicillin contain corn steep liquor, a by-product of maize starch production. This contains the nitrogen source and other growth factors. The energy source is usually lactose. The production of penicillin is stimulated by the addition of phenylacetic acid, but the concentration is critical as it is toxic to the fungus. A supply of oxygen is required, as the growth of *P. chrysogenum* and the production of penicillin require aerobic conditions. Oxygen is supplied by means of filter-sterilised air pumped into the fermenter.

Penicillin is excreted into the medium and so is in solution with various other substances. The process of extraction, purification and subsequent chemical modification of penicillin, referred to as **downstream processing**, involves solvent extraction. The penicillin is extracted, firstly by filtration, which separates fungal material from the medium, then by using solvent extraction to isolate the penicillin. The pH is first reduced to 2.0 to 2.5 and the penicillin is extracted into an organic solvent such as amyl acetate. Penicillin is then re-extracted back into an aqueous buffer at pH 7.5, concentrated, and then crystallised. Penicillin produced in this way is known as penicillin G, which may be converted to semi-synthetic penicillins, as a means of overcoming the problems of penicillin-resistant strains of bacteria. Penicillin G is first converted into 6-amino penicillanic acid (6-APA) using the enzyme penicillin acylase. 6-APA is then chemically modified by adding various chemical side groups, to produce a range of substances known collectively as semi-synthetic penicillins, such as amoxycillin, ampicillin and methicillin. The structures of penicillin G and some examples of semi-synthetic penicillins are shown in Figure 2.10.

Antibiotics belong to a group of chemical substances referred to as **secondary metabolites**. These are substances which are produced by microorganisms, towards the end of the growth phase and into the stationary phase. The synthesis of secondary metabolites is very dependent on the culture conditions, particularly the composition of the medium. It appears that they are not essential for the growth and reproduction of the microorganism, and often accumulate in the growth medium in relatively high concentrations. In order to maximise the production of penicillin, nutrients such as nitrogen sources may be added to the medium towards the end of the growth phase – this is referred to as fed-batch culture.

penicillin G
(benzylpenicillin)

penicillin V
acid-resistant

methicillin
resistant to β-lactamase

ampicillin
broad-spectrum
acid-resistant

oxacillin
resistant to acid and
β-lactamase

Figure 2.10 The structure of penicillin G and some examples of semi-synthetic penicillins

Similar techniques for the large scale culture of microorganisms can be used for the production of enzymes, such as α-amylase by the bacterium *Bacillus licheniformis*. Many enzymes used in industry are extracellular and are excreted by the microorganisms into the culture medium.
Extracellular enzymes can be extracted from the medium by a process of filtration, to remove the microorganisms, then reverse osmosis is used to separate the enzyme from other components of the medium. The extraction of **intracellular enzymes** is more complex and involves cell disruption, followed by purification of the enzyme. Cells are disrupted to release the enzymes, by treatment with detergents, or lysozyme (an enzyme which digests some bacterial cell walls), or by mechanical methods. After removal of cell debris, the enzyme may be purified and concentrated using, for example, ammonium sulphate solution which will precipitate the enzyme from solution.

Plant and animal cell culture

The principles involved in the culture of microorganisms can be applied to the culture of cells and tissues obtained from plants and animals. Essentially, this involves the culture of suitable cells under aseptic conditions, in complex media which have been specially formulated for this purpose. The

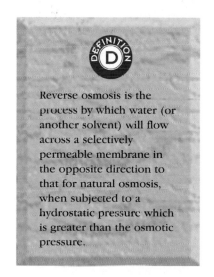

Reverse osmosis is the process by which water (or another solvent) will flow across a selectively permeable membrane in the opposite direction to that for natural osmosis, when subjected to a hydrostatic pressure which is greater than the osmotic pressure.

maintenance of strict aseptic conditions is essential in cell and tissue culture, as any contaminating microorganisms are likely to grow very much faster than the plant or animal tissue.

Plant tissue culture involves the growth of isolated cells or tissues in controlled, aseptic conditions. It is possible to use plant tissue culture to regenerate whole plants, a technique referred to as **micropropagation**. One of the uses of this technique is to propagate rare, or endangered, species which are difficult to propagate using conventional methods of plant breeding. Micropropagation is also used to produce ornamental plants, including pot plants, cut flowers and orchids on a large scale for commercial purposes. The techniques of plant tissue culture are also used to eliminate pathogens from infected plants, for example in the production of virus-free plants, such as carnations and potatoes. There are a number of different types of plant tissue culture, including:

- embryo culture, cultures of isolated plant embryos
- organ cultures, cultures of isolated organs including root tips, stem tips, leaf buds and immature fruits
- callus cultures, which arise from the disorganised growth of cells derived from segments of plant organs, such as roots.

The isolated part of the plant used for culture is referred to as the **explant**, which can be almost any part of the plant. The tissue used as the explant is grown in culture media containing a variety of mineral nutrients, plant growth regulators such as auxins and cytokinins, sucrose, and amino acids.

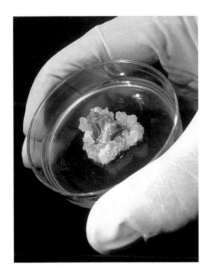

Figure 2.11 Plant tissue culture on a sterile agar medium

A callus culture may be grown by removing tissue from a suitable plant organ such as a carrot. This must be surface sterilised by placing it in a suitable chemical disinfectant such as 20 per cent sodium hypochlorite solution. The carrot is then washed with sterile distilled water and, using sterile instruments and aseptic technique, a segment of tissue removed from the cambium. This is then transferred to a flask containing sterile culture medium and incubated at 25 °C. The explant will grow to form a mass of cells known as a callus, which has a distinctive crumbly appearance. The callus can be maintained indefinitely by sub-culturing the tissue onto fresh medium every 4 to 6 weeks, or the callus can be transferred to a medium containing a different balance of plant growth regulators and can be induced to form structures known as embryoids, from which complete plants can be regenerated. This method has a number of important commercial applications, such as the rapid propagation of agricultural crop plants.

Animal cells which are cultured can be derived from explants of the four basic tissue types, epithelial, connective, nervous or muscular tissues. Some of these cells, such as lymphocytes (derived from connective tissue), can be grown in a suspension culture, similar to bacteria in a liquid medium. Most normal mammalian cells, however, grow attached to a surface and form a single layer of cells referred to as a **monolayer**. Tissues removed from an animal are usually treated with a proteolytic enzyme, such as trypsin, to separate individual cells. The cells are then washed in sterile saline solutions and transferred to a suitable sterile container, such as a plastic flask, containing a culture medium. The cells settle on the bottom of the flask, attach, and begin to divide to form a monolayer. The cells can be removed, by treatment with trypsin, and used to inoculate fresh medium. In this way, the growth of some cells can be maintained indefinitely, whereas some cells have a finite capacity for growth.

Media used for animal cell culture are usually very complex and contain a range of amino acids, glucose, vitamins and other enzyme cofactors, inorganic ions and buffers to maintain the pH. Serum may also be added to the media to provide essential growth factors. Antibiotics, such as penicillin and streptomycin, are sometimes added to the media to inhibit the growth of bacteria which may accidentally contaminate the cultures.

Suggestions for practical work
Suitable practical activities which illustrate the principles of tissue culture can be found in:
Biological Sciences Review, Volume 10, Number 3, January 1998, published by Philip Allan;
Practical Biotechnology – a guide for schools and colleges, 1993, published by the National Centre for Biotechnology Education, University of Reading

3 Use of microorganisms in biotechnology

Exploitation of microorganisms

Biotechnology is a relatively modern word, though its roots lie at the very beginnings of human civilisation. In this chapter, we see how the art of making beer, bread, yoghurt and cheese developed and has grown with different human societies through the centuries. It was the work of Pasteur in the mid-19th century that led to an understanding of the activities of microorganisms and gave an insight into their role in traditional food processing activities. This signalled the beginnings of microbiology as a science (see Chapter 1). Today, at the end of the 20th century, biotechnology is concerned with exploiting the activities of living organisms, especially microorganisms. It embraces several disciplines – microbiology, biochemistry and chemistry, cell biology, genetics and biochemical engineering – to ensure the activities of these organisms can be geared to production, often in large scale processing. Biotechnology has medical and agricultural applications, and is involved in waste treatment, the production of fuels and in the food and beverage industries.

We can, for convenience, distinguish between traditional fermentations and more recent developments in biotechnology concerned with genetic modification. Development of techniques which enable the modification of DNA means that scientists can, in a very precise way, alter the genome within an organism or transfer genetic information from one organism to another. The organism can be modified to produce a particular protein, or certain metabolic processes can be altered deliberately. In a **transgenic** organism, DNA from different species has been combined. For example, a human gene could be inserted into a bacterium or yeast, or a bacterial gene could be inserted into a crop plant – in other words, the species barrier can be crossed. If we view the whole range of applications for biotechnology we can see that its future potential is considerable and is likely to escalate as we move into the 21st century.

Figure 3.1 Simple cheeses from Yunnan, south-west China, where herds of yaks, cattle, sheep and goats graze the mountain grassland and the people are essentially pastoralists. The shape of the cheeses is determined by the conical baskets in which the curds drain while the cheese is being made.

Industrial uses of enzymes

Later in this chapter some examples of lactic acid fermentations and activities of yeasts are described. Traditional fermentations exploit microorganisms and their enzymes to modify foods. These fermentations continue to be very important on an industrial scale, but a newer industry of **enzyme technology**, using enzymes harvested from microorganisms, has grown up alongside them and now has many commercial applications. Enzymes produced from fungi and bacteria can be isolated from the growth media and purified as necessary. When used in an industrial process, the enzyme is often immobilised which improves its stability, allowing the enzyme to be re-used and the products to be more easily separated. Microbial enzymes are now used in a wide range of industrial processes, including the production of paper, textiles, leather and biological detergents. They are also being applied in medicine, for diagnosis and treatment. Methods for bulk production and separation of microbial enzymes are outlined in Chapter 2 and here we describe some applications of these enzymes in the food industry.

Cellulases

Cellulases break down cellulose to shorter chains, then to the disaccharide **cellobiose** and to β-glucose. Fungal sources include species of *Aspergillus*, *Trichoderma*, and *Penicillium*. These cellulases currently have limited use in the food industry, but can be used to produce more fermentable sugars in brewers' mashes, to clarify orange and lemon juices, to improve the release of colours from fruit skins, to clear the haze from beer and to tenderise green beans. When used with lignases, cellulases may have great potential in the processing of waste materials such as straw, sugarcane bagasse, sawdust and newspaper, to produce sugars (**saccharification**) from the cellulose contained in these materials. First the wood must be treated to remove lignin. Sugars from wood can then be fermented to alcohol (ethanol). A yeast (*Candida* spp.) has been grown on wood pulp hydrolysed by cellulases to produce single-cell protein (SCP).

One use of cellulases in the food processing industry is to clear pipes in processing machinery.
What sort of material might have accumulated in the pipes and how would cellulases help in its removal?

Lignin is extremely resistant to both chemical and enzymatic degradation, though some microorganisms (mainly fungi) produce enzymes which can act on lignin or lignin linked to cellulose. Where is lignin found in plants? How might ligninases (enzymes which degrade lignin) be important in natural ecosystems?

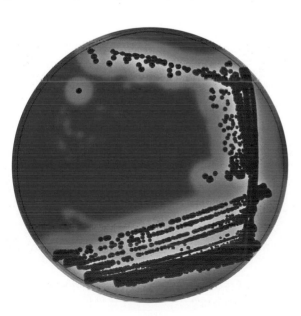

Figure 3.2 Colonies of Escherichia coli which have been genetically engineered to express a cellulase gene isolated from a cellulose digesting bacterium. They are growing on a gel that contains cellulose. Absence of the red dye indicates cellulose digestion.

USE OF MICROORGANISMS IN BIOTECHNOLOGY

Figure 3.3 (a) laboratory investigations on the effect of pectinase on the yield of apple juice; (b) small-scale version of apple crusher; (c) small apple press.

Pectinases

Pectinases degrade pectins (polysaccharides found within plant cell wall structure) to shorter molecules of **galacturonic acid**. This can be broken down further to sugars and other compounds. Pectin itself is able to form jellies, which are useful in some products (such as the setting of jam), but are undesirable in fruit juices and other liquids. Pectinases are obtained commercially from fungi, particularly species of *Aspergillus* and *Penicillium*. Bacterial and other fungal pectinases are significant in soft rot of fruits and vegetables, contributing here to spoilage and decay. Probably the biggest industrial use of pectinases is in the extraction and clarification of fruit juices. Pectinases are added to crushed fruit such as apples and grapes to increase the yield of juice extracted and improve colour derived from fruit skins. Wines, vinegar and other liquids which contain suspended pectic material can be clarified with pectinases. They act by removing some of the pectin around charged protein particles, which then clump together and settle out of the liquid. Pectinases can also be used to prevent jelling when fruit juices are concentrated.

Amylases

Amylases hydrolyse **glycosidic** (**glucosidic**) **bonds** in polysaccharides such as starch and glycogen, converting them to **dextrins** (shorter length chains of glucose units) or to **maltose**. Enzymes in the group act in different ways on the α-1,4 links, and on the α-1,6 links within the polysaccharides. These

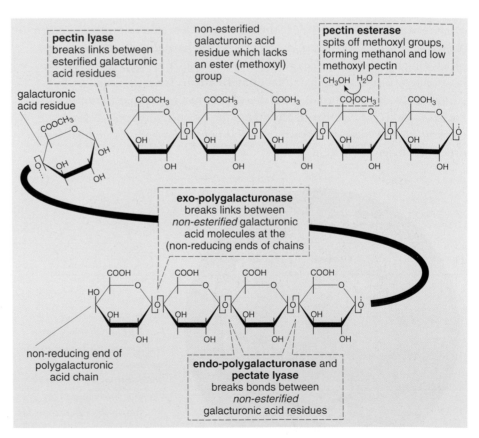

Figure 3.4 Activities of pectinases – a group of enzymes which break down complex pectin molecules to simpler residues. Pectinases are important in the fruit juice industry

amylases include **amyloglucosidase** (glucoamylase) which hydrolyses the 1,4 links and the 1,6 links at the branches in the starch molecule. Terminal **glucose** units are removed from the end of the chain one at a time, rather than giving the intermediate dextrins or maltose. **Pullulanase**, also known as debranching enzyme, hydrolyses the α-1,6 links at the branching points in the polysaccharide. Commercial sources of these enzymes are obtained from bacteria (*Bacillus* spp.) and fungi (*Aspergillus* spp., *Rhizopus* spp. and *Streptomyces* spp.). Fungal amylases are used to clarify fruit juices, wines and beer by removing suspended starch. In bread-making and brewing, addition of amylases can yield more sugars from the starch in flour or the barley grains. An important commercial use is the conversion of starch to sweet glucose syrups which are used generally as sweeteners in the food industry as well as in bread-making and brewing. Altering the balance between amyloglucosidase and the fungal α-amylase can produce different proportions of glucose and maltose. A higher proportion of glucose is useful for fermentation whereas higher maltose is more useful in preparation of jam and confectionery. Further conversion of glucose, using the enzyme glucose isomerase, yields fructose which is sweeter than both sucrose and glucose. High fructose corn syrups (HFCS), derived from hydrolysing corn (maize) starch, have become a major source of sweeteners in foods and drinks in the USA.

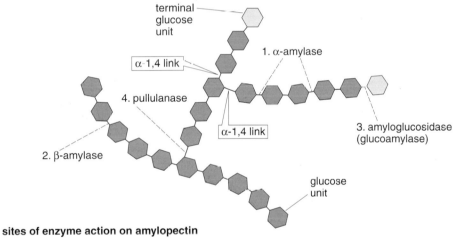

sites of enzyme action on amylopectin

1. α-amylase – hydrolyses internal α-1,4 glucosidic links, forming dextrins, maltose, glucose
2. β-amylase – hydrolyses alternate α-1,4 glucosidic links, forming maltose
3. amyloglucosidase – hydrolyses terminal α-1,4 glucosidic links, forming glucose
4. pullulanase – hydrolyses α-1,6 glucosidic links (at branching points), forming dextrins

Figure 3.5 Activities of amylases, a group of enzymes which act on glucosidic bonds and break down complex carbohydrates, such as starch and glycogen, to simpler residues

Proteases

Proteases are known as proteinases and peptidases. They hydrolyse **peptide bonds** in proteins and peptides, acting either within the peptide chain or removing amino acid residues sequentially from one or other end of the chain. Fungal sources include species of *Aspergillus*, *Mucor* and *Rhizopus*. *Bacillus* spp. provide a source of bacterial enzymes. Proteases account for about 50 per cent of the commercially-used microbial enzymes. Some fungal enzymes are used in cheese-making as a substitute for rennet (see page 43) to help clot milk. Other uses for microbial proteases include clarification of fruit

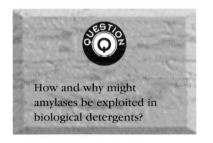

How and why might amylases be exploited in biological detergents?

juices and beer by removing the protein haze, thinning egg white so that it can be filtered before drying, tenderisation of meat, digestion of fish livers to allow better extraction of fish oil and modification of proteins in flour used for bread-making. Another important use of extracted bacterial proteases is in biological detergents. The protease contributes to the breaking down of protein stains when washing clothing.

Lactase

Lactase (β-**galactosidase**) breaks down the disaccharide lactose, the sugar in milk, to **galactose** and **glucose**. Commercially produced microbial lactases are obtained from *Aspergillus* spp. and the yeast *Kluyveromyces* spp. An important application of lactase is to hydrolyse lactose in milk to make it suitable for people who are intolerant of lactose (see *The Organism and the Environment, 2nd edition*). Such people are unable, as adults, to digest lactose, so the undigested lactose is likely to be fermented by bacteria in the large intestine, resulting in nausea, abdominal pain and diarrhoea. Glucose and galactose both taste sweeter than lactose, so lactase is used to increase sweetness in products such as ice cream and to produce a sweet syrup from whey, which might otherwise be discarded as a waste product from the cheese industry (see pages 42 to 44). In ice cream manufacture, use of lactase also removes lactose which crystallises at low temperatures and would contribute to a 'sandy' texture. (See *Practical section*, pages 79 to 80.)

Lipases

Lipases hydrolyse lipids (glycerides) to **fatty acids** and **glycerol**. Some are specific in that they release the fatty acids only from one or two positions on the glycerol of the molecule; others are more general. In the food industry, they are sometimes used to enhance the ripening of certain cheeses and also to help break down fatty materials in waste, particularly in the dairy industry and fast-food outlets. Lipases are also incorporated into biological detergents to digest and remove fat stains on clothing and other household materials.

Lactase activity is inhibited by the end-product (galactose) it produces. In the industrial processing of whey, the enzyme may be immobilised on cellulose acetate fibres.
Devise an experiment you can do in the laboratory to illustrate immobilisation. How would immobilisation help overcome the problem of end-product inhibition?

Which enzymes are used in the clarification of fruit juices, wines and beer, and how does each act?

Food and drink

The art of processing food stems from the very beginnings of human civilisation, as humans changed from a hunter–gatherer way of life to more permanent, settled communities. The making of bread, cheese, wine and beer are food-processing practices which are central to many human societies, traditional and modern. The origins of different discoveries were probably accidental, but the benefits were doubtless soon appreciated. Food could be kept longer, transported or stored from one season to the next. A wider range of flavours became part of the diet and alcoholic liquor, particularly, assumed an importance in ceremonies and social gatherings.

The ancient art of modifying raw harvested food has evolved into the modern food and drink industry. The processing is highly mechanised, rigorously monitored and controlled to ensure uniformity of end-products, many of which are destined for world-wide distribution. The impact of biotechnology in

Table 3.1 *Examples of some industrial enzymes, their sources, properties and uses*

Enzyme group	Enzyme trade name	Organism source	Optimum temperature and pH	Industrial applications
cellulase	Celluclast® 1.5L	fungus *Trichoderma reesei*	65 °C pH 5.0	• brewing – reduces wort viscosity (added at mashing in stage) • breakdown of cellulosic material for production of fermentable sugar
pectinases	Pectinex™ Ultra SP-L	fungus *Aspergillus niger*	35 °C • pH 5.5	disintegrates cell walls • for treatment of fruit mashes (especially apples and pears) – increased press capacity and higher juice yields
α-amylase	Termamyl®	bacterium *Bacillus licheniformis*	95 °C pH 7.0	useful because of its heat stability • alcohol industry – thinning of starch in distilling mashes • brewing – liquefaction, simpler cooking programme • sugar industry – breakdown of starch in cane juice, so less starch in raw sugar
α-amylase glucoamylase	Amylo-glucosidase AMG	fungus *Asperigillus niger*	60 °C to 75 °C pH 4.0	• sweeteners – production of glucose syrup • wine and beer – removal of starch haze • bread – improved crust colour • low carbohydrate beer – production of fermentable glucose
protease	Neutrase®	bacterium *Bacillus subtilis*	45 °C pH 6.0	• brewing – fortifies malt proteases (barley) • baking – softens wheat gluten (e.g. for biscuits)
lactase (β-galactosidase)	Lactozyme®	yeast fungus *Kluyveromyces fragilis*	48 °C pH 6.5	• produces low-lactose milk – suitable for lactose-intolerant people • sweeter so less sugar need be added to drinks • yoghurt – sweeter, longer shelf-life • ice-cream – no lactose crystals, improves scoopability and creaminess • whey – conversion to syrup for use as sweetener
lipase	Lipolase™ (uses DNA technology)	fungus *Asperigillus oryzae*	35 °C pH 7–11 (wide range)	• in detergents – removing fat stains (e.g. frying fat, salad oils, sauces, cosmetics)

the modern food and drink industry can be illustrated by the activities of microorganisms in:

- fermentations
- harvesting of microorganisms as biomass to be consumed as food for humans or feed for animals
- production of extracellular enzymes (see page 53 and Chapter 2).

In addition, increasingly, we are seeing the use of genetically modified organisms in the food industry.

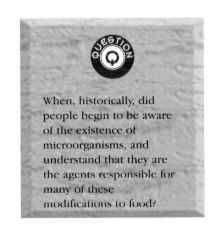

When, historically, did people begin to be aware of the existence of microorganisms, and understand that they are the agents responsible for many of these modifications to food?

Fermentations

Fermentations are a significant way of modifying raw fresh food. The fermented product has properties that are different from the original material. The fermentation may enhance the flavour or alter the texture, palatability and digestibility of the food, and there may be changes in the nutritional content. These changes often make the food safer because it is then unsuitable for the growth of other microorganisms. Sometimes toxins are eliminated. Traditionally, fermentation of various foods has provided an important means of preservation, though today other methods, such as freezing, have become more important. The term **fermentation** is used in two senses. In the narrower, biochemical sense, fermentation is a form of **anaerobic respiration**, and is a means by which organisms, or cells within organisms, obtain energy from an organic substrate in the absence of oxygen. In the broader sense, the term is used to describe a very wide range of processes carried out by microorganisms. Many yield products of commercial importance. Some fermentations involve anaerobic respiration, but many do not.

Lactic acid fermentations are carried out by a range of bacteria, including species of *Lactobacillus*, *Leuconostoc* and *Streptococcus*. These lactic acid bacteria convert carbohydrate to lactic acid, sometimes with other products. The carbohydrate is usually lactose, but other sugars are also utilised. The lowered pH provides an environment unsuitable for the growth of many microorganisms, which is why these fermentations offer a means for reducing spoilage of foods. This gives the foods improved storage properties as well as alterations in flavour and texture. Lactic acid fermentations are the basis of the dairy industry, and are also involved in the production of sauerkraut (fermented cabbage), some sausages and salamis and sourdough bread. **Yeasts**, particularly of the genus *Saccharomyces* and also *Kluyveromyces*, are important in the **alcoholic fermentation** of sugars (mainly glucose), which is the basis of the wine and brewing industries and is also used in bread-making.

Fermented milk in dairy products – yoghurt and cheese

Fermentation of milk, into yoghurt and into cheese, is both a very ancient and a widespread practice. In Europe, we are most familiar with yoghurt from cow's milk, or from sheep, but milk from other mammals, including goats, buffalo and camels is also used. Probably the first yoghurt was from the Middle East. Milk being carried under warm conditions doubtless became sour, developed agreeable flavours and could be kept longer than fresh milk, with obvious advantages to nomadic people. A portion of a successful ferment might have been used again to start the next batch, effectively selecting suitable strains of bacteria.

Yoghurt

In the modern industrial preparation of yoghurt, whole milk may be **blended** with skimmed milk or skimmed milk solids. Starch or sugar may be added to give a different flavour or consistency. Sometimes the milk is heated to allow evaporation and make a thicker yoghurt, though on a large scale the viscosity (thickness) of the end-product is controlled by the initial mixture of milk and solids. The fat content can be adjusted by removing fat or by adding cream. The milk is **homogenised** to disperse the fat as small globules, then heated to 88 to 95 °C for between 15 and 30 minutes to **pasteurise** the milk. The high temperature and time used are necessary to kill bacteria which may be active at relatively high temperatures (described as *thermophilic* bacteria). Milk inevitably carries a microflora from the udder, and these contaminants could act as competitors in the yoghurt making process.

The starter culture includes two species of bacteria which enhance each other's activities. First, *Lactobacillus bulgaricus* acts on milk protein, converting it to small peptides and amino acids. These stimulate the growth of the second species, *Streptococcus thermophilus*. *S. thermophilus* in turn produces formic acid which stimulates growth of *L. bulgaricus*. *L. bulgaricus* is mainly responsible for the conversion of lactose to lactic acid and production of some ethanal (acetaldehyde) which, with other compounds, contributes to the flavour. The culture is incubated at 40 to 45 °C for 3 to 6 hours (or at 32 °C for 12 hours), then cooled rapidly to prevent further bacterial fermentation. At the end of the fermentation, the lactic acid concentration is about 1.4 per cent and the pH is between 4.4 and 4.6. The thickening of the yoghurt is the result of the coagulation of proteins.

In the **set method** for making yoghurt, the homogenised milk with starter culture is poured into the final containers and incubated. More commonly, the mixture is **stirred** during the fermentation then poured into containers at the end of the process. Fruit or other flavours may be added, either at the start of incubation for set yoghurt, or at the end for stirred yoghurt. The fruit may introduce unwanted yeasts or other microbial contaminants into the yoghurt. Fruit yoghurts are often protected by adding sugar, giving a higher osmotic potential and lower pH. At the same time the sugar sweetens the yoghurt.

The popularity of yoghurt comes in part from its improved digestibility. It is particularly valuable for lactose-intolerant people, but if additional milk solids are added to thicken the yoghurt, some lactose may remain in the final product. Variations in the end-product come from using cultures of different organisms.

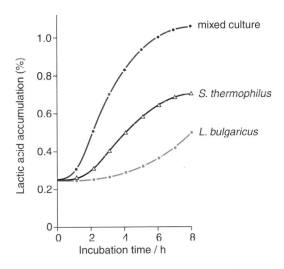

Figure 3.6 Preparation of yoghurt and the effect of different clture organisms. Comparison of two single strain cultures, Streptococcus thermophilus *and* Lactobacillus bulgaricus, *and a mixed culture of both strains*

Skimmed milk is added to milk in making yoghurt, to help thicken it and improve its nutritional value, but this also increases its lactose content. Only about 15 per cent of this lactose sugar is used during the fermentation. Pre-treatment of the milk with lactases reduces the lactose and the yoghurt sets more rapidly. Devise a practical investigation you could carry out to compare the rate of setting of yoghurt, made from lactose-reduced and normal milk. What other benefits might there be in making yoghurt from lactose-reduced milk?

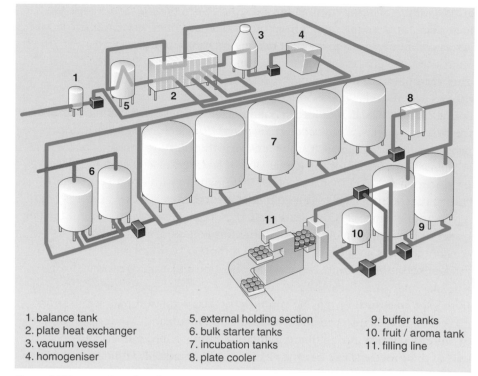

1. balance tank
2. plate heat exchanger
3. vacuum vessel
4. homogeniser
5. external holding section
6. bulk starter tanks
7. incubation tanks
8. plate cooler
9. buffer tanks
10. fruit / aroma tank
11. filling line

Figure 3.7 Preparation of yoghurt on an industrial scale

A multiplicity of names are used for yoghurt-type preparations throughout the world. Find out where the following fermentations are eaten or drunk, what milk each uses, and how they differ in their processing from the yoghurt described in this chapter:
Acidophilous milk; Amaas; Buttermilk; Chal; Dadih; Filmjolk; Kefir; Kumiss; Lassi; Mast; Raita; Yakult; Yiaourti.

Cheese

Making cheese is probably the oldest way of preserving the nutrients in milk over a long period. It probably started by carrying milk in sacks made from the stomach of a sheep, cow or other domesticated mammals. Over the centuries a wide variety of traditional cheeses has developed. Differences in flavour and texture depend on the source of milk and local methods used in the later stages of treating and maturing the cheese.

The basic steps in making cheese can be summarised as follows:
- coagulation of protein in the milk to form curds
- removal of whey (a watery liquid)
- ripening or maturation (may include pressing).

It is the final step that introduces the widest range of variations in texture (soft or hard) and flavour (such as mild, mature or blue) to the cheese. Control of the microorganisms present is the key to the wide range of individual cheeses that are produced.

In present day commercial production of cheese, such as English Cheddar cheese, the early stages are similar to that in yoghurt, namely **standardisation of fat content** and **homogenisation**. The milk is then **pasteurised** by heating to 72 °C for 15 seconds, cooled rapidly to 31 °C and transferred to the cheese vat. In the next stage, known as **ripening** (of the milk), the starter culture of lactic acid bacteria is added. This usually contains *Streptococcus lactis*, often with *S. cremoris* or other species depending on the flavour required. Conversion of lactose to lactic acid by the bacteria lowers the pH and milk proteins (mainly casein) begin to **coagulate**. Further curd formation results from the addition of **rennet**. Traditionally, this is an extract from the stomach of young calves (or from other young mammals). The active enzymes are **chymosin** (about 90 per cent) and **pepsin** (about 10 per cent). Of interest to vegetarians is the increasing use of genetically modified microorganisms to produce chymosin (see page 55).

It takes about 45 minutes for the milk to clot. The curds are then separated from the liquid whey and further processed in several steps to form the cheese:

- the curds are cut into small pieces (about the size of a pea) - this releases some whey
- the curd is heated to about 39 °C and stirred continuously to release more whey in a process known as **scalding**
- stirring is stopped, the curds settle (known as **pitching**), the whey is drained off
- the curd particles begin to knit together and the curd is cut into large blocks which are stacked and turned – more whey drains off
- **cheddaring** involves turning and piling the blocks to achieve the desired texture – it can be done by hand or mechanically
- cutting with an electric mill (**milling**) further reduces particle size
- salt is added in varying amounts – this helps to preserve the cheese and bring out desired flavours

If making a hard cheese, the salted curd is packed into a mould and then pressed, which further reduces the water content.

During a period of maturation, which may last up to a year or more, various enzymatic processes continue, resulting in changes in flavour and texture. Lipases convert lipids to glycerol and fatty acids – butyric acid is one that has a characteristic flavour. Proteases degrade proteins to amino acids – in some cheeses this results in a more liquid texture. Further enzymatic action produces a variety of amines, aldehydes and ketones which contribute to the flavour. The final pH of cheeses varies from about 4.5 in cottage cheese to 6.9 in a matured camembert.

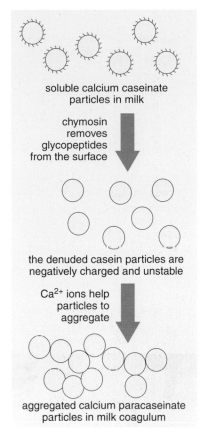

soluble calcium caseinate particles in milk

chymosin removes glycopeptides from the surface

the denuded casein particles are negatively charged and unstable

Ca^{2+} ions help particles to aggregate

aggregated calcium paracaseinate particles in milk coagulum

Figure 3.8 Converting casein to curds – how milk protein coagulates

Figure 3.9 Commercial production of cheese: (a) stirring the curds on the conveyor; (b) packing the cheese into moulds (farmhouse cheese making); (c) the 'Blockformer' process another faster method of pressing, used in mass production of cheese. The curds are taken under vacuum to the top of a vertical tower (the blockformer). As they pass down the column, further whey is removed under vacuum and pressure and the curds consolidate. At the bottom of the tower, 20kg blocks are cut off and vacuum sealed in polythene. The cross-section of the tower is the same as that of the finished block of cheese.

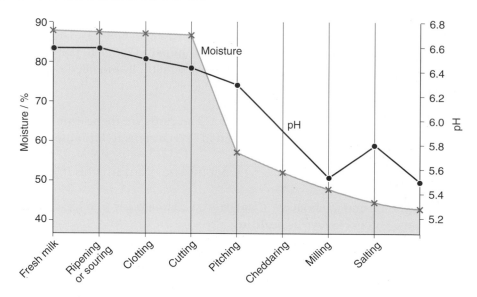

Figure 3.10 Changes in moisture and in pH during the different stages of making cheddar cheese. Making cheese is essentially a dehydration process, allowing the fat and casein in the milk to be concentrated 5 or 10 times their original concentration. Fermentation of lactose to lactic acid contributes to the lowering of the pH

Figure 3.11 Different varieties of cheese.

Table 3.2 *Features of some cheese varieties – differences in the type of milk, the microorganisms used in the fermentation or ripening stages, the extent of dehydration and the time for maturation have led to the development of hundreds or thousands of local cheese varieties*

Type	Examples	Features of cheese variety
very hard	Parmesan	made from semi-skimmed cow's milk; pressed, dried and matured for 1 to 4 years
hard	• Cheddar, Leicester • Cheshire • Gruyere, Emmental (Swiss cheeses)	• (see text for description) matured 6 to 12 months • more crumbly than Cheddar; matured 3 to 6 months • carbon dioxide produced by bacteria collects in pockets, giving the characteristic holes
semi-hard (white)	Lancashire Wensleydale	• whole cow's milk used; matured 1 to 4 months; • mild flavour; crumbly
semi-hard (white-brined)	Feta	from cow, sheep or goat milk; matured in brine for 3 to 10 weeks
semi-hard (blue)	Gorgonzola, Roquefort (sheep), Stilton (cow)	cow, sheep, or goat milk used (for Gorgonzola); the mould *Penicillium roqueforti* added to curds before removing the whey; mould grows through the cheese; fungal spores give the blue colour; characteristic flavour due to enzymatic conversion of fats to fatty acids and ketones
soft	• Cottage cheese • Brie, Camembert • Mozzarella	• high moisture; unripened; eaten fresh • high moisture; surface ripened due to mould and bacterial growth • from buffalo or cow milk; curd pulled to long pliable mass; eaten fresh or after 1 to 2 weeks

Yeast and brewing

Brewing beer and making wine are among the oldest, and perhaps most pleasurable, of biotechnologies. It is not difficult to see how a pile of surplus discarded cereal grains or fruit began to ferment, and the liquor which seeped out was enjoyed for its flavour and alcoholic effects. These alcoholic beverages are appreciated by countless individuals and have had an important influence on successive cultures over the centuries. Brewing of beer was known to the Egyptian and Babylonian civilisations at least 4000 years ago, and probably earlier. In Britain, beer was known before the Romans came and the art of brewing developed further in the Middle Ages. At that time, there was no understanding of the microbiology of what was going on, but the secrets of the process were jealously guarded. Unknown to the early drinkers, the alcohol made these beverages microbiologically safer to drink than water of doubtful quality and the yeast provided some vitamins of the B complex. Hops were introduced to Britain in the 15th century and by then, the traditional brewing processes used today were more or less established.

The basic brewing process involves 'malting' of barley grains by soaking in water and allowing them to germinate, followed by fermentation of the sweet liquor by yeasts. The modern brewing industry produces either **ale**, fermented with 'top-fermentation yeast' (see page 47) or **lager**, associated more with Europe than Britain. Lagers are fermented with a 'bottom-fermentation yeast'. Other beers, such as sorghum beer which is made in Africa mainly from sorghum, millet and maize, are brewed using similar principles.

Barley (*Hordeum vulgare*) is a cereal crop which grows widely in temperate zones as well as in the tropical highlands of Africa. The main stages in the brewing of beer from barley can be summarised as follows:
- malting
- milling and mashing
- addition of hops and boiling
- fermentation
- maturation
- packaging for distribution and sale.

The barley grain contains stored starch in the endosperm. Most yeasts cannot utilise the starch so the first stage of the brewing process is the conversion of starch to soluble sugars. To prepare the barley **malt**, the grains are **steeped** in water and allowed to **germinate**. The steeping is generally done in a vertical tank for about 2 days. Air is passed through the water to ensure conditions are aerobic. After about 12 hours, the water is drained out to give a period of 'air-rest' which allows oxygen from the surrounding air to dissolve in the film of water around the grain. This gives faster and more uniform germination. The barley is immersed in water again and this process may be repeated several times. Traditionally the barley is then spread out on a malting floor. A wooden shovel is used to turn the germinating barley to provide air which allows respiration to continue and accumulated carbon dioxide to be removed. Temperatures should be maintained at about 15 °C. After about 5 days, rootlets have appeared in the sprouting barley which is now called **malt**. During the

Curds . . . and whey – waste it or use it?
Whey is a watery by-product of the cheese industry. It contains about 5 per cent lactose and less than 1 per cent of non-casein proteins. It could be wasted, but there is increasing interest in using it to manufacture other commercial products. One process uses the enzyme lactase immobilised on glass beads to produce sugars and syrups which are then used in the confectionery industry for soft-centred chocolates and for cake icings. In Eastern Europe whey is fermented to Prokllada for a sweet or savoury drink.

What environmental problems could arise if waste whey is discharged from factories into nearby waterways? Which sugars are produced from lactose and what are the advantages of using immobilised enzymes in commercial manufacturing processes?

USE OF MICROORGANISMS IN BIOTECHNOLOGY

germination process, some degradation of starch and proteins occurs, but the main purpose of malting is to allow development of enzymes which become important in the subsequent stages. This is stimulated by release, from the embryo of the plant, of the growth substance **gibberellic acid** which acts on the aleurone layer (see *Systems and their Maintenance*, Chapter 3). Germination is stopped by heating to between 65 and 80 °C, a process known as **kilning**. This temperature kills the embryo but does not inactivate the enzymes. It also improves the flavour and dries the malt, allowing storage.

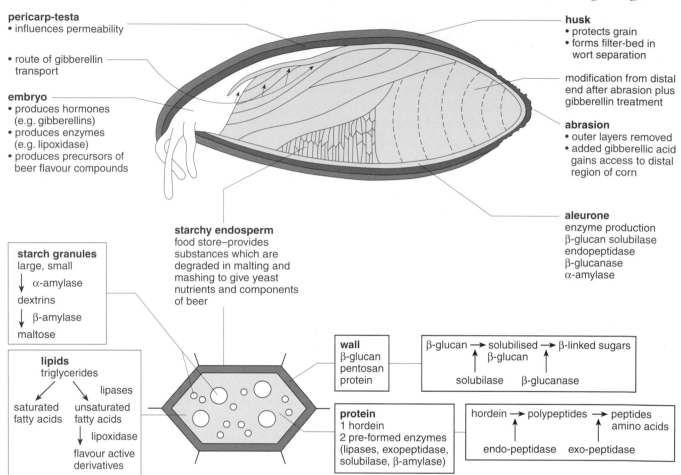

pericarp-testa
• influences permeability

• route of gibberellin transport

embryo
• produces hormones (e.g. gibberellins)
• produces enzymes (e.g. lipoxidase)
• produces precursors of beer flavour compounds

husk
• protects grain
• forms filter-bed in wort separation

modification from distal end after abrasion plus gibberellin treatment

abrasion
• outer layers removed
• added gibberellic acid gains access to distal region of corn

aleurone
enzyme production
β-glucan solubilase
endopeptidase
β-glucanase
α-amylase

starchy endosperm
food store–provides substances which are degraded in malting and mashing to give yeast nutrients and components of beer

starch granules
large, small
↓ α-amylase
dextrins
↓ β-amylase
maltose

lipids
triglycerides
lipases
saturated fatty acids   unsaturated fatty acids
↓ lipoxidase
flavour active derivatives

wall
β-glucan
pentosan
protein

β-glucan → solubilised → β-linked sugars
                β-glucan
        ↑   ↑
solubilase   β-glucanase

protein
1 hordein
2 pre-formed enzymes (lipases, exopeptidase, solubilase, β-amylase)

hordein → polypeptides → peptides amino acids
        ↑   ↑
endo-peptidase   exo-peptidase

Figure 3.12 Changes within the barley grain during the malting process

Figure 3.13 Female flowers (cones) of the hop plant. These give 'bitter' its bitter flavour.

Figure 3.14 Oast houses. Hops were traditionally dried in such buildings.

The brewing process continues by **milling** the malt grains to break the starchy endosperm into a gritty flour known as **grist**. This is then mixed with hot water, usually at about 65 °C, in a large vessel, the **mash tun**. Some other unmalted ground cereals may also be added. During this **mashing** stage, enzymes from the original barley convert starch into soluble sugars. The resulting extract is a sweet liquor called wort. After 1 to 3 hours, the **wort** is drained through the bed of husks from the barley and retained. The spent barley grains are removed and have some value as cattle feed.

The female flowers (cones) of hops (*Humulus lupulus*) give the characteristic bitter flavour to beer. In Britain, hops are harvested in September then dried in a warm current of air in an oast house or hop kiln. Hop picking used to be done by hand and urban families migrated to the countryside for a working 'holiday', but now most picking is done mechanically. The wort and hops are boiled together for about 2 hours in a large vessel, known as a **copper**, and, if required, some sugar is added. The boiling stops further enzyme activity, provides a means of sterilising the liquid and allows other changes including extraction of tannins and oils from the hops which contribute to flavour. The boiled wort is cooled and passed to the fermenting vessel. The spent hops are discarded and may be used as a fertiliser.

The wort contains sugars and other nutrients and is now ready to be **fermented** by yeasts. Various strains of **brewers' yeasts** are used and added as prepared cultures. The choice depends on the type of beer to be produced. After an initial lag phase, the yeasts grow rapidly then, as the oxygen is used up, the yeasts switch to anaerobic fermentation and the sugars are converted to ethanol and carbon dioxide. Heat is given off so the fermentation vessel must be cooled. *Saccharomyces cerevisiae* is used for ales and this strain of yeast produces a froth on the surface of the fermenting vessel, described as 'top-fermentation'. Fermentation takes about 5 days at 20 °C. For lager, the 'bottom-fermenting' yeast strain *S. carlsbergensis* is used. Fermentation takes between 7 and 14 days at lower temperatures (5 to 15 °C) and because less froth is produced, the yeast sinks to the bottom. At the end of the fermentation, the yeast is removed, either by skimming from the surface or by collecting the sediment from the bottom. This surplus yeast is used in the food industry, to produce yeast extract and products such as *Marmite*.

The wort has now become beer, but requires further conditioning before it is ready to be drunk. Traditionally this has been done in wooden casks, over a period of a few weeks (or months for lagers), in cool temperatures. During this time, there are changes in flavour and some secondary fermentation takes place. In many modern breweries, the maturation takes place in large storage vessels. The beer is then centrifuged to remove cell debris, artificially carbonated with carbon dioxide, filtered, bottled or transferred to small barrels and often pasteurised to improve the keeping quality. The range of beers available differs in colour, sweetness, flavour and alcoholic strength (see Table 3.3).

Figure 3.15 (a) Mash tun at Masham Brewery, North Yorkshire; (b) some small fermentation vessels; (c) froth on the surface during beer fermentation.

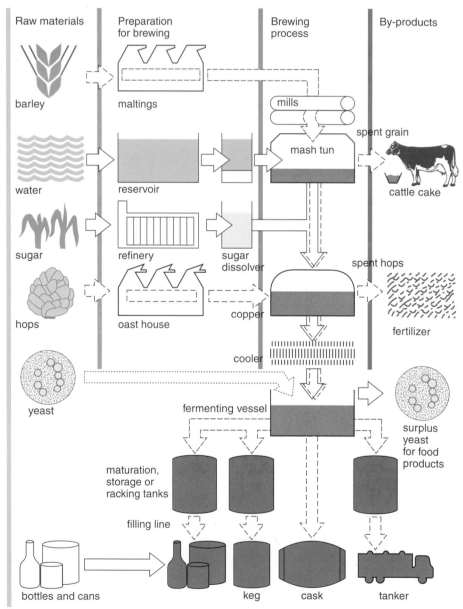

Figure 3.16 Summary of the brewing process, showing inputs and by-products at different stages

Table 3.3 *Different types of beers. The OG values give a measure of the strength of the beer. OG stands for Original Gravity and indicates the fermentable matter, but does not necessarily represent precisely the final level of alcohol. Very roughly, 1008 = 2 per cent, and 1040 = 10 per cent alcohol*

Ales – fermented with a top-fermentation yeast		
pale ales	OG 1032–48	made from pale malts, strongly hopped, little sweetness
bitter	OG 1032–48	draught pale ales
brown ales	OG 1032–48	made from malts which give deeply coloured beer, sweeter and less hopped than pale ales
mild	OG 1032–40	draught equivalent of brown ales (sometimes pale)
stout	OG 1032–55	darkest ale, some very bitter with no sweetness, others sweet
barley wine	OG 1065–1100	very strong pale ale
Lagers – fermented with bottom yeast		
pale	OG 1032–48	made with pale malt, no sweetness, distinctive hop flavour and aroma
dark	OG 1042–55	made with darker malts, sometimes slightly sweet

Yeast and the production of dough for bread

Today, most bread is made from wheat flour, though rye and other flours can be used. A simple unleavened (flat) bread can be made by mixing flour with water then baking it. Using yeast in the mixture produces a lighter, leavened bread, now consumed widely throughout the world. The yeast used by bakers is a suitably selected strain of *Saccharomyces cerevisiae*. The process requires the mixing of flour with water, salt and yeast, often with the addition of some sugar. Enzymes (α and β amylases) in the wheat flour hydrolyse amylose and amylopectin in the starch, mainly to maltose and some glucose. The yeast utilises the sugars, converting them to carbon dioxide and some ethanol. The carbon dioxide is responsible for the raising of the bread dough. As the gas expands it becomes trapped in the dough, making it lighter.

During the mixing, or **kneading**, the dough is kept at a temperature of about 26 °C. At first the yeast grows and produces carbon dioxide. In a second kneading, the dough is 'knocked back', letting some gas escape and causing the dough to tighten up. It is then cut and put into tins or moulds for baking. Typically the whole process of 'proving' the dough can take up to 4 hours. On **baking** at about 232 °C for 15 minutes or longer (depending on the type of loaf), the carbon dioxide is expelled leaving holes in the hardened dough and the ethanol escapes. The high temperatures kill the yeast, preventing further action.

The secret to the structure of the bread lies in the properties of the proteins in wheat flour. Collectively the proteins are called **glutens**, made up mostly of gliadin and glutenin. A good bread flour, described as 'hard', has a protein content of 10 to 14 per cent, whereas softer flour has a protein content below 10 per cent and is more suitable for making biscuits or pastry. When the water is mixed with the flour, the proteins absorb water to form an elastic gluten complex. This allows the dough to stretch and retain the bubbles of carbon dioxide. The strength of the gluten is derived from the way the long branched protein chains link together, to form a sort of network. This is enhanced by links between –SH (sulphydryl) groups from the amino acid cysteine, forming long branched chains which give the dough its strength. The kneading process is important for several reasons – it mixes the ingredients allowing even dispersion of the carbon dioxide bubbles, but also plays a part in the modification of the proteins, allowing the chains to line up alongside each other and form the cross-links. **Improvers** such as **ascorbic acid** (vitamin C) are sometimes added to bread flour to speed up the processing time. During the intense mixing, the ascorbic acid is oxidised to dehydroascorbic acid. It then interacts with the –SH groups by removing hydrogen and forming disulphide S–S bridges very rapidly. This helps the dough structure to form and tighten quickly, giving a reduced fermentation time. Large scale commercial bread-making processes also utilise higher levels of yeast. Other improvers have been used to bleach flour to make it whiter, though consumer preferences are now swinging in favour of unbleached flour.

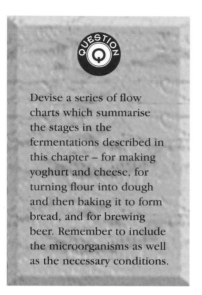

Devise a series of flow charts which summarise the stages in the fermentations described in this chapter – for making yoghurt and cheese, for turning flour into dough and then baking it to form bread, and for brewing beer. Remember to include the microorganisms as well as the necessary conditions.

Figure 3.17 Simple unleavened bread being prepared in an open-air market in Yunnan, south-west China.

Mycoprotein

Fungi have a high protein content and grow rapidly, so offer considerable potential as a source of protein in the human diet or as supplements to animal feeds. They can grow on a wide range of substrates, including waste materials from industrial or other processes. Some edible large fungi are already well-known for their eating qualities – these include the common edible mushroom (*Agaricus bisporus*), the oyster mushroom (*Psalliota* spp.) and truffles (*Tuber melanosporum*). During the 1950s to 1970s, there was active research into ways of utilising microorganisms as a source of food, to produce **single cell protein** (**SCP**). The term SCP is used to describe protein derived from microbial cells (such as yeasts, other fungi, algae and bacteria), though the microorganism producing the protein is not necessarily 'single-celled'. The whole organism is harvested and consumed, rather than using the products of their fermentations or other processing. Exploitation of SCP production offers a way of increasing the available protein for consumption by humans and by livestock, and could be valuable particularly in areas where the land is infertile or the climate inhospitable. While SCP production may have potential for feeding the ever increasing world population, in practice only a few schemes have proved to be commercially successful – the most successful for human consumption being **mycoprotein**, marketed under the name of *Quorn*™.

Mycoprotein is obtained from the growth of the filamentous fungus *Fusarium graminareum*. Glucose syrup is used as the carbon source, gaseous ammonia supplies the nitrogen and salts are added. Wheat or maize starch is used as the source of glucose, though other starchy crops can be used. Choline is added to encourage growth of long hyphae and biotin (a vitamin) is also required. The *F. graminareum* is grown in a 1300 litre continuous culture fermenter, at 30 °C and pH 6. The ammonia gas helps to maintain the pH and oxygen gas is supplied to keep conditions aerobic.

The fast growth rate of microorganisms leads to a high RNA content which is unsuitable for consumption by humans and other animals. In humans, excess nucleic acids are converted to uric acid which is not excreted by the kidneys, resulting in the accumulation of uric acid crystals in the joints giving gout-like symptoms. In the normal production of mycoprotein, after fermentation the RNA content is around 10 per cent which is too high, but this can be reduced to about 2 per cent by using thermal shock and the action of ribonucleases. After RNA reduction, the mycelium is harvested continuously on a horizontal filter bed and the filter cake which is recovered can be stored at 18 °C for long periods.

The harvested mycoprotein is a mat of interwoven fungal hyphae which can then be formulated into a range of food products. Its filamentous nature gives it a texture and 'bite' similar to that of meat. Mycoprotein itself tastes bland but can be flavoured to resemble chicken and is added to pies, burgers and cold slicing meats. Its composition compared to that of lean beef is given in Table 3.4.

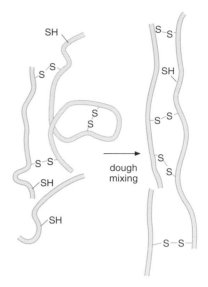

Figure 3.18 Bread dough and the kneading process. Molecular changes in the gluten proteins and the formation of cross-links between sulphydryl groups contribute to the properties of the dough which enable it to trap carbon dioxide gas

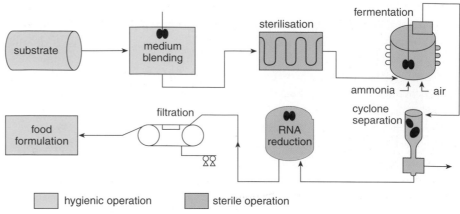

Figure 3.19 Outline of the process for production of mycoprotein

Other SCP products are given in Table 3.5. In developing commercial schemes, palatability is an important feature if the SCP is to be used for human consumption, or ways must be found to incorporate the SCP into familiar foods and so increase protein content. Ultimately, the success depends on the economics of microbial production compared with protein production from animals and plants in conventional agriculture and horticulture. Table 3.6 lists some of the perceived advantages of SCP production, and some of the disadvantages that have come to light with industrial schemes already attempted.

Table 3.4 *Comparison of mycoprotein and beef*

Feature	Mycoprotein	Beef
protein	44.3%	68.2%
dietary fibre	18.3%	0.0%
fat	13.0%	30.2%

Table 3.5 *Microorganisms as food - some of the attempts to utilise single cell protein (SCP)*

Microorganism	Substrate used	Product, use, comments
Fusarium graminearum (filamentous fungus)	glucose syrup + gaseous ammonia, salts, biotin	mycoprotein, filamentous fungus, texture similar to meat products
Candida lipolytica (yeast)	alkanes (*n*-paraffin) + supply of gaseous ammonia, phosphate, other salts	alkanes Toprina-G, used as feed additive – no longer made
Methylophilus methylotrophus (bacterium)	methanol + ammonia, phosphate, other salts	'Pruteen' for animal feed – no longer made
Spirulina sp. (blue-green bacterium)	photosynthesis – grown in open ponds	dried and fed to animals, becoming popular as a 'health food'; eaten by people around Lake Chad in Africa, also by Aztecs in ancient Mexico

Figure 3.20 Mycoprotein - marketed as Quorn, on sale in the UK.

Table 3.6 Single cell protein (SCP) – some advantages and disadvantages

Advantages of SCP
• fast growth rate, high yield in relatively short time
• production throughout the year, regardless of season
• range of substrates can be utilised, including waste materials from industrial processes
• high protein content compared with some other sources (such as soya bean or fish meal)

Disadvantages of SCP
• may be deficient in certain amino acids, such as methionine or other sulphur-containing amino acids, which are essential for humans or other animals
• microbial cell walls indigestible by humans and non-ruminant mammals
• the high RNA content in microbial cells unsuitable for humans because they lack the enzyme which would break it down
• concern that toxins may persist in the growth medium when using wastes from industrial processes

Production of chymosin (microbial rennin)

In cheese-making, **chymosin** (rennin) is the main enzyme involved in the coagulation of casein, the protein in milk. Traditionally, the source of chymosin was **rennet**, an extract from the abomasum (stomach) of young calves, or sometimes from kids or lambs. In the 16th century, rennet was prepared by cutting strips of the stomach of young calves and steeping these in warm milk or brine to extract the rennet. By the late 19th century the first industrial preparation of calf rennet was established by a Danish chemist. Calves destined for consumption as veal were used, so they were not sacrificed specifically for the extraction of the enzyme. More recently, in the 1960s, because of changing eating patterns, there was concern that there would be a world-wide shortage of rennet for commercial cheese production. This led to pressure to find alternative sources of rennet and to develop substitutes to keep up with the demand.

Bovine rennet from adult cattle can be used as an alternative to calf chymosin, but the bovine extract contains a higher proportion of pepsin and gives a lower yield of cheese. Certain fungi produce proteases which can clot milk proteins. **Fungal enzymes** are now used in more than one third of cheese produced world-wide. Three fungi used for production of the enzymes are *Mucor miehei*, *M. pusillus* and *Endothia parasitica*. Compared with calf chymosin, the fungal enzymes are more stable, but this can be a disadvantage in cheeses which have a long maturing stage (e.g. Cheddar cheese) because degradation of the milk proteins continues. To counteract this, these enzymes can be destabilised, using oxidising agents, so that they behave in a way similar to the more successful calf chymosin. Fungal enzymes are used widely in production of cheese for vegetarians.

DNA technology has provided further substitutes for calf rennet. The first microorganisms capable of making chymosin were produced in 1981, using *Escherichia coli*. Now chymosin is produced from genetically modified yeasts, including *Kluyveromyces lactis* and *Saccharomyces cerevisiae*. Precisely the same DNA code as in the calf is incorporated into the microorganism, so the enzyme produced is identical to that from calves. Expert tasters can detect no differences between the cheeses produced using chymosin from genetically modified organisms and that from extracted calf rennet. The enzymes actually have fewer impurities and their behaviour is more predictable. At first there was resistance to accepting cheese made with the involvement of genetically modified organisms (GMOs). Before being released for general consumption, there was rigorous testing of the products. The enzymes used for cheese produced in this way have been approved by the relevant regulatory bodies and by the Vegetarian Society. Such cheese is on sale in several countries, including the UK.

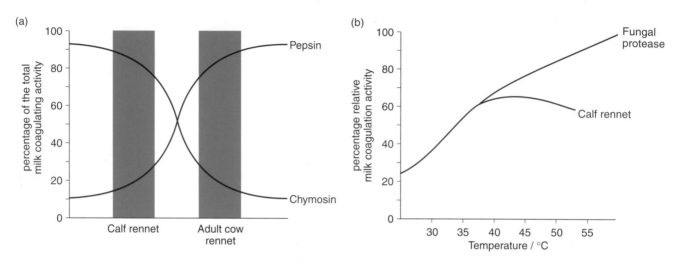

Figure 3.21 (a) Changes in relative proportions of chymosin and pepsin in rennet from young calf to adult cow, showing relatively more chymosin in calves and higher pepsin in adult bovine rennet; (b) Differences in behaviour of calf rennet and fungal protease – influence of temperature

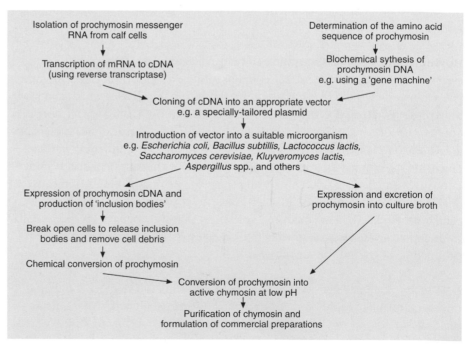

Figure 3.22 Stages in the production of calf chymosin by genetically modified microorganisms. Prochymosin is an inactive precursor of chymosin

Medical applications

Through the centuries different medicines or treatments have been used in attempts to combat disease, pain or discomfort in people and their domestic animals. More than 2000 years ago, the Chinese were using mouldy soya bean curd to help cure infections such as boils. Interest in plants, and the development of botany as a science, was often through the perceived healing properties of plants as well as their exploitation for crops and food. Some of the treatments used certainly had a sound but unrecognised biological basis even though they may have been disguised within the rituals of folklore. Others depended more upon the intervention of religious powers. Nearly 2000 years ago in ancient Greece, the medical practices linked with Hippocrates, promoted proper diet and exercise as preventative medicine to avoid disease.

By the end of the 20th century, applications of medical science have assumed a dominant role in modern society. Healthcare and advice now start before conception, continue through pre-natal stages and childhood and carry on during adulthood through to old age. We are tested, advised, protected or cured for many potential or actual medical conditions. We can appreciate the impact of medical science and hygiene measures by looking at the enormous reduction of infectious disease on a global scale. Biotechnology infiltrates many parts of medical practice and research continues to look for ways of giving relief to non-infectious diseases, including inherited and degenerative diseases. Medical treatments which are dependent upon biotechnology include therapeutic products, such as antibiotics and hormones, and the production of vaccines. Biotechnology is involved in prenatal diagnosis of genetic diseases and in the development of immunological techniques for clinical diagnosis. At the molecular level, DNA probes can be used for disease identification and there is now considerable interest in the potential for gene therapy (see *Systems and their Maintenance*, Chapter 6). Some ways in which microbial activities are exploited in medicine are illustrated by production of antibiotics and human insulin, and the use of monoclonal antibodies.

A range of milk-clotting enzymes is available. Maxiren is pure chymosin, produced from a genetically modified yeast (*Kluyveromyces lactis*) and *Fromase* is a fungal enzyme.

Devise a practical investigation you could carry out to compare the effectiveness of these enzymes with that of calf rennet, in their ability to clot milk. Why might calcium ions or differences in pH and temperature affect the rate of setting of the curds?

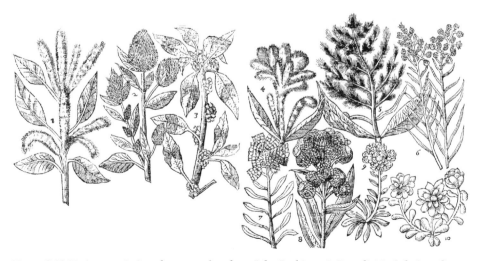

Figure 3.23 Various varieties of amaranthus from John Parkinson's Paradisi in Sole Paradisus Terrestris, 1629. "Divers suppose the flowers of these plants doe helpe to stay the fluxe of blood in man or woman, because that other things are red or purple doe performe the same."

USE OF MICROORGANISMS IN BIOTECHNOLOGY

Antibiotic production

Like so much in biotechnology, the therapeutic properties of some fungal preparations were known from ancient times and used in the treatment of wounds. The benefits, however, tended to be dismissed as folklore rather than being taken seriously by the medical profession. In 1929, Alexander Fleming discovered penicillin almost accidentally. He was growing plates of pathogenic bacteria and noticed that when contaminated with the mould *Penicillium notatum*, growth of the bacteria was inhibited. Penicillin was isolated from the medium and found to be responsible for the effect. While the potential for medical applications was appreciated at the time, the stimulus for finding a means of purification followed by large-scale production and medical use came during the 1939–1945 war. Since the 1940s, penicillin and other antibiotics of fungal origin have produced a revolution in the history of medicine to the extent that many major infectious diseases have largely been brought under control.

The term **antibiotic** was originally used to describe substances produced by microorganisms that could be used to kill or inhibit growth of certain other microbes. The term was introduced in the 1940s to distinguish the newly produced **penicillin** from other synthesised chemicals used for chemotherapy. Since that time, the meaning of the term has broadened to include natural antibiotics, which are modified to become semi-synthetic, and other entirely synthetic antimicrobial compounds.

Since penicillin was first introduced, many thousands of metabolites from fungi and from bacteria have been screened for antibiotic activity. Of these, relatively few have proved useful medically, but those which have are very successful. Some antibiotics are used in food preservation and non-medically in animal feeds. Their action on other microorganisms may be described as **microbicidal** if they kill the other microbe, or **microbistatic** when they inhibit or retard growth of other microorganisms. The nature of their action may vary with concentration of the antibiotic or depend on other factors. Generally, Gram positive bacteria are more sensitive to antibiotics than Gram negative bacteria. The effectiveness of an antibiotic is described as **broad spectrum** when it acts on a wide range of Gram positive and Gram negative bacteria, whereas **narrow-spectrum antibiotics** are more specific. These can, nevertheless, be useful medically because they target a limited range of microbes, sometimes only one species. The mechanism of action differs, depending on the antibiotic and microbe affected, but includes interference with cell-wall synthesis (in bacteria) or with membrane function (in fungi). Antibiotics are produced as secondary metabolites (see page 31), so are not considered to be essential to the growth and metabolism of the producer organism.

Commercial production of penicillin now uses *Penicillium chrysogenum* rather than *P. notatum*, and strains have been selected which give very much higher yields than the early production methods. Waste liquor from steeping corn (maize) has been used extensively as the growth medium. Other carbon sources, such as mixtures of glucose and lactose, are now used though the

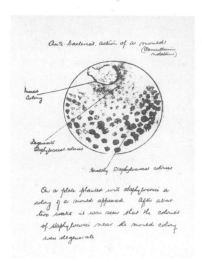

Figure 3.24 Notes on and drawing of the original culture plate of the fungus Penicillium notatum, made by Alexander Fleming in 1928

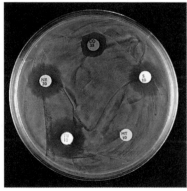

Figure 3.25 An antibiotic sensitivity test. The agar plate has been streaked with a culture of E. coli and sensitivity discs, impregnated with antibiotics, placed on the agar. After incubation, clear inhibition zones are seen around discs which contain antibiotics to which the organism is sensitive. No inhibition zone is seen around the disc containing methicillin, showing resistance to this antibiotic

Table 3.7 *Antibiotics act differently and sometimes selectively on their target organisms. This table summarises the sites of action and mechanisms at the cellular level for some antibiotics*

Site of action	Example of antibiotic	Mechanism of action
cell wall synthesis	penicillin, cephalosporin, vancomycin	• inhibit bonds that strengthen the bacterial cell walls, which include peptidoglycan molecules cross-linked with peptide chains. The antibiotic interferes with formation of peptide bonds • effective only when bacteria are growing
protein synthesis	chloramphenicol, tetracycline, erythromycin, streptomycin	• often bind to the bacterial ribosomes in preference to the mammalian ribosomes, thus interfering with and inhibiting protein synthesis • may lead to synthesis of abnormal proteins. Streptomycin distorts the ribosome, causing an error in reading the genetic code so the wrong amino acid is inserted into the peptide chain
nucleic acid synthesis	rifampicin, anthracyclines	• rifampicin binds selectively to RNA polymerase in bacteria in preference to that in mammals, so prevents initiation of transcription • anthracyclines inhibit DNA synthesis in all cells, especially rapidly growing cancer cells. Effective as anti-cancer drugs, but also kill some normal cells
cell membrane function	amphotericin B, nyastin (used against fungi) polymixin (used against bacteria)	• damage cell membranes so interfering with function • amphotericin has affinity for ergosterol, a sterol in fungal cell membranes, and distorts the lipid bilayer. This probably opens the channels in the membrane, allowing contents to leak to the exterior thus destroying the cell

corn-steep liquor is still useful for providing a source of growth factors. Little penicillin is produced during the growth phase, but as the carbon source becomes depleted, production of penicillin increases. The fungus is grown in large fermenters with a capacity up to 200 000 litres, in aerobic conditions at temperatures between 25 and 27 °C and pH between 6.8 and 7.7. Production is by batch culture, and when complete the fungal biomass is separated from the liquor. The liquor is cooled and the penicillin is extracted using a solvent (see Chapter 2).

The effectiveness of antibiotics as chemotherapeutic agents is becoming less because of the increasing resistance to antibiotics shown by different populations of microorganisms that are normally, or were formerly, sensitive to them. **Antibiotic resistance** can be defined as the acquired ability of a microorganism to resist the effects of an antibiotic to which it is normally susceptible. Some organisms are naturally resistant, whereas others may develop the characteristic through mutation. In some cases, resistance may be acquired by genetic exchange (conjugation, transduction or transformation in bacteria) with those that already have resistance. Spread of resistance through the population is encouraged by selection of resistant strains in the presence of antibiotics in their environment. The characteristic of resistance may have arisen in microbes as a sort of defence mechanism to neutralise or destroy their own antibiotics.

Spread of antibiotic-resistant strains is certainly linked to high use of antibiotics. Often they are used inappropriately or unnecessarily. Since the 1950s, which signalled the start of widespread use of antibiotics, dosages of antibiotics to combat certain diseases have been increased and in some cases

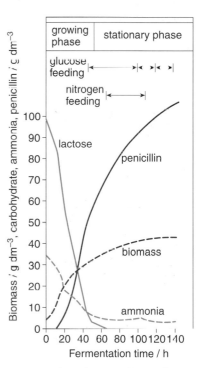

Figure 3.26 Production of penicillin by Penicillium chrysogenum. *There is little production during the growing phase but the main production occurs as the cells enter the stationary phase and can be prolonged for several days by maintaining the supply of appropriate nutrients*

treatment has become ineffective. This can be illustrated by treatment for gonorrhoea, caused by *Neisseria gonorrhoeae*, for which penicillin is no longer effective due to high incidence of resistance to it. Inevitably resistance is likely to develop, but its spread could be minimised by reducing use of antibiotics to essential cases only. They should certainly be avoided for treatment of minor infections. A further cause of the spread of antibiotic resistance has come from the use of antibiotics in agriculture, where they are used in animal feeds, both to enhance growth rate and as a prophylactic to prevent development of diseases. In Europe, there is careful regulation so that antibiotics used in animal feeds are not also used for medical treatment of humans. Modification of the chemical nature of the antibiotic molecules, say by production of semi-synthetic analogues, has in some cases given a drug which is effective against otherwise resistant strains. Such drugs can be used, at least for a short time, until resistant strains catch up with them!

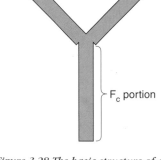

How might the practice of using antibiotics in feed for livestock affect the processing of milk into yoghurt and cheese?

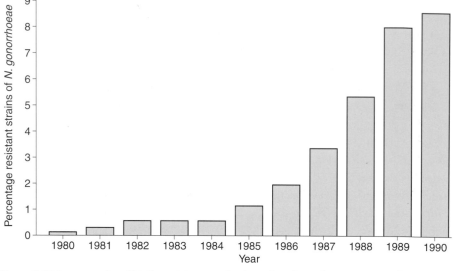

Figure 3.27 Increase of antibiotic resistance – the data show how the percentage of reported cases of gonorrhoea caused by antibiotic-resistant strains of Neisseria gonorrhoeae *has increased over a 10-year period (data from Atlanta, Georgia, USA)*

Monoclonal antibodies

Antibodies, also referred to as immunoglobulins, are substances produced by B lymphocytes. All antibodies have the same basic structure, but part of the molecule, the antigen-binding portion, is variable. Each antibody will bind specifically with only one antigen. For example, the antigen-binding portion may bind to a specific pathogenic microorganism and another part of the antibody molecule, referred to as the Fc portion, then binds to a receptor on a phagocytic cell which allows the pathogen to be ingested and destroyed by the phagocyte. This specificity of antibodies for a particular antigen makes them useful for a number of medical purposes, including the detection of minute quantities of antigens in the diagnosis of tumour cells or identification of pathogenic microorganisms.

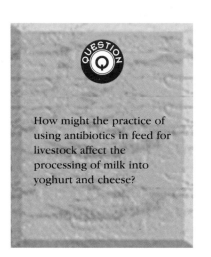

Figure 3.28 The basic structure of an antibody

In the body, lymphocytes are capable of making several million different antibodies and attempts to isolate antibodies from an animal result in a mixture of antibodies (known as a polyclonal mixture) with only limited usefulness because of its variable composition. In 1975, Kohler and Milstein discovered a method of producing cells which are capable of continuously secreting a single type of antibody, known as a **monoclonal antibody**, to a chosen antigen. This technique has resulted in the technology which is used to produce large quantities of single types of antibodies.

The method involves producing 'immortal' cells, which synthesise a single antibody, so that production can be maintained indefinitely. Monoclonal antibodies can be produced against any substance which the immune system recognises as an antigen. An animal, usually a rat or a mouse, is injected with the chosen antigen and, after about 3 weeks, the animal is killed and its spleen removed. The spleen contains antibody-secreting cells and other cells associated with the immune system. A cell suspension is prepared from the spleen and the lymphocytes separated by centrifugation. Lymphocytes have a finite life-span in culture and therefore have limited usefulness for the industrial production of antibodies.

Lymphocytes are made immortal by fusing them with abnormal cells, known as myeloma cells (malignant lymphocytes), which are capable of indefinite growth. Lymphocytes from the spleen are fused with myeloma cells in a medium which contains polyethylene glycol (PEG), a substance which encourages fusion of the cell surface membranes and subsequent fusion of the nuclei. These fused cells are known as **hybridomas**. Only a small proportion of the cells fuse successfully, so this treatment results in a mixture of cells containing lymphocytes, myeloma cells and hybridomas. The hybridoma cells are selected by growing in a culture medium containing a mixture of hypoxanthine, aminopterin and thymidine (HAT medium). Lymphocytes and hybridoma cells are able to grow in this medium, but any remaining myeloma cells die. The lymphocytes die naturally after 1 to 2 weeks, leaving only the hybridoma cells.

Some of the surviving hybridoma cells have the same antibody-producing capability of the original spleen cells. These cells are identified by testing for the secretion of the desired antibody. This results in the production of a clone of cells, derived from a single hybridoma, which can grow indefinitely and produce a monoclonal antibody. The process for the production and isolation of hybridoma cells is shown in Figure 3.29.

Hybridoma cells can be grown in an industrial fermenter, similar to that described in Chapter 2. The cells are grown in batch culture, then separated from the medium by centrifugation and the antibody then extracted and purified, using techniques of chromatography. This technique offers the possibility of producing a kilogram of antibody from a single culture.

One specific use of monoclonal antibodies is for the early detection of pregnancy in commercial pregnancy test kits. These involve the detection of a hormone, human chorionic gonadotrophin (HCG), in the urine. HCG is secreted by the blastocyst and can be detected in the urine about 10 to 14 days after fertilisation. Pregnancy test kits contain a test strip which is impregnated with an HCG-specific monoclonal antibody. The test strip is dipped into a

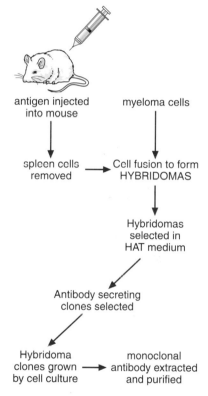

Figure 3.29 Production and isolation of a monoclonal antibody-secreting hybridoma

urine sample and, if HCG is present, it binds to the HCG monoclonal antibody to form an HCG–antibody complex. A second antibody is then used which reacts with the HCG–antibody complex and produces a colour change.

Microbial production of human insulin

The human hormone insulin is a protein, normally produced in the β cells of the islets of Langerhans in the pancreas. In the body, insulin is involved in the regulation of the glucose level in the blood (see *Systems and their Maintenance*, Chapter 3). People who show deficiency of insulin production suffer from a form of **diabetes** (diabetes mellitus). Large amounts of sugar are found in the blood (**hyperglycaemia**) and in the urine (**glycosuria**). The condition is usually accompanied by thirst, excessive production of urine and loss of weight. In severe cases, when supplies of sugar to the brain fall too low, the person may go into a coma which can lead to death. This type of diabetes can normally be kept under control by careful regulation of the carbohydrate content of the diet and through daily administration, by injection, of the hormone insulin.

Insulin was first extracted from the pancreas in 1921. Since then, extracts from the pancreases of dogs, and later from cattle and particularly pigs, have been used widely as a source of insulin to treat people with diabetes. These animal sources have certainly saved the lives of many diabetics, but the insulin is not identical to that from humans and sometimes there are unpleasant long-term and short-term side-effects. To maintain a continuous supply requires slaughter of many animals, which some people do not support, and the extraction and purification procedures are difficult.

Attempts were made in the early 1980s to use DNA technology to produce human insulin from microorganisms. The first human insulin, known as *Humulin*, produced from genetically modified bacteria, was licensed for use in 1982 (see *Cell Biology and Genetics*, Chapter 7). This insulin was produced from *Escherichia coli*, and since then other microbes, including bakers' yeast (*Saccharomyces cerevisiae*), have been genetically modified to produce insulin. These microbial sources of human insulin overcome the limitations of obtaining sufficient insulin from animals and ensure cheaper supplies of insulin that can be considered to be identical to the natural human hormone.

The insulin protein is relatively small, so rather than locate and isolate the insulin gene from a human source, one approach has been to synthesise a length of DNA that codes for the correct amino acid sequence in each of the A and B polypeptide chains. These DNA sequences are then incorporated into the genetic material in plasmids which are inserted into separate bacterial cultures of *E. coli*. The synthesised polypeptide chains are recovered from the culture medium and treated chemically to form the disulphide bonds and make the insulin protein.

An alternative strategy is used in genetically modified yeast. The first stage in the normal cellular synthesis of insulin is to produce pro-insulin, in which the A and B chains are joined by another polypeptide, the C chain. The full

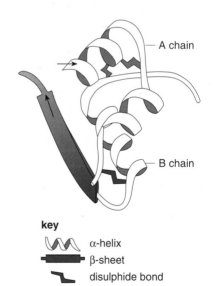

key

ㅿㅿ α-helix

▬▬ β-sheet

⌐ disulphide bond

Figure 3.30 The insulin molecule consists of two polypeptide chains – the A chain is made up of an α-helix, the B chain has an α-helix and a β-sheet. The two chains are linked by disulphide bonds. The A chain has 21 amino acids and the B chain has 30 amino acids. Compared with humans, insulin from pigs has one amino acid different, and that from cattle has two amino acids different

molecule of pro-insulin cannot be secreted from yeast cells, but this problem
has been overcome by producing a 'mini-insulin' in which the A and B
polypeptide chains are joined by a short, synthetic C chain. This C chain is
different from that in the human pro-insulin but the mini-insulin which is
synthesised by the yeast can be secreted from the cells. The short synthetic
C chain is then removed chemically to give a protein which is identical to
human insulin. As with the first approach, the DNA sequences which code for
the polypeptide chains are synthesised artificially before being inserted into
the yeast.

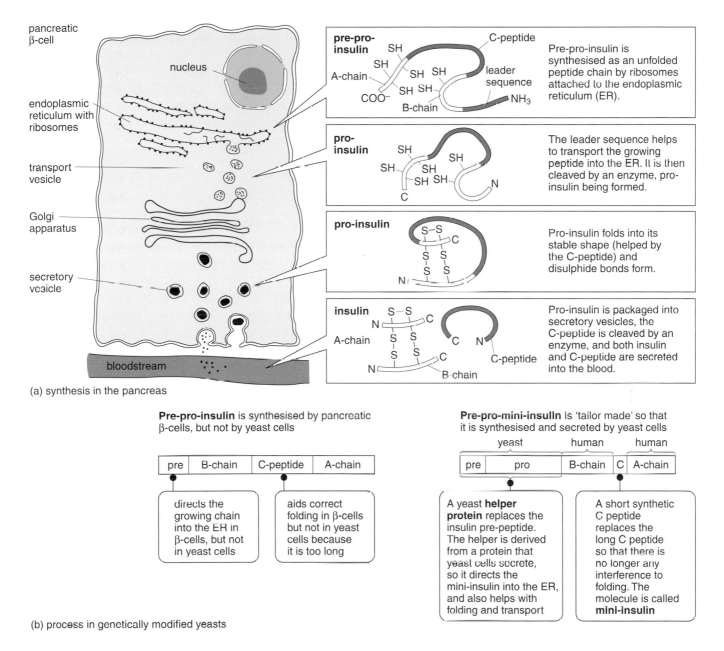

(a) synthesis in the pancreas

(b) process in genetically modified yeasts

*Figure 3.31 Synthesis of insulin in the pancreas and from genetically modified yeasts. In the pancreas, β cells synthesise pro-insulin,
a precursor of insulin. Pro-insulin consists of the A and B chains connected by a C peptide, which is made up of 30 amino acids.
The C peptide is removed by an enzyme to give active insulin. When using yeast cells to synthesise human insulin, a shorter synthetic
C peptide is inserted as the normal one is too long to allow folding of the molecule inside the yeast cell*

Production of human insulin from microbial sources was the first therapeutic product to be produced by DNA technology, but the potential for producing other medically valuable products is enormous. These include blood proteins, other human hormones and vaccines. Some are already available for general use whereas others are at the stage of research and testing before approval for human use.

Agriculture

Biotechnology has already found a niche in modern agriculture, with notable applications in the defence against disease through animal vaccines, exploiting the potential of transgenic animals, in microbial control of insect pests and use of micropropagation. Biotechnology also offers huge potential for diversifying the products which can be obtained from plants or plant cell cultures. Here we look at some specific examples which employ microbial cultures with or without enzymes to enhance the natural activities of microorganisms. We also explore briefly the use of gene technology and its potential for improvement of crop plants.

Silage production

Grazing crops of grass, or grass mixed with other herbage, is usually the most economical way of feeding farm livestock, such as cattle or sheep. However, growth of grass is often seasonal – in temperate climates because the winters are too cold and in other places because grass may not grow, for example, in the dry season. Traditionally, making **hay** has been a means of conserving grass by drying, but increasingly making **silage** (ensiling) is used as an alternative way of conserving grass. Compared with hay, the nutritional value of silage is higher with respect to carbohydrate and protein content. Another advantage is that silage may be made with a range of young leafy herbage and under conditions that would be unsuitable for hay-making.

Table 3.8 *Comparing grass, hay and silage – typical values of important features in relation to feeding of livestock*

Feature	Grass (grazed)	Hay	Grass silage	Maize silage
dry matter / %	21	86	29	30
energy as ME / mj kg^{-1}DM	11.2	9.2	10.7	11.2
protein as DCP / g kg^{-1}DM	93	73	105	127
pH	–	–	4.2	4.0

DM (or dry matter): represents the material left after all water is removed and is used as the basis for calculating feeds for livestock
ME: the metabolisable energy, or the amount the animal can make use of
DCP: digestible crude protein, or the protein that can be utilised by the animal

Silage is fermented grass, effectively pickled in its own juice. The cut grass contains sugars which are fermented by **lactic acid** bacteria under anaerobic conditions to give **lactic acid**. The pH falls to about 4.0 which is low enough to prevent spoilage of the product by other microbes. When ready to make silage, the grass and other herbage is cut and wilted for several hours. This allows it to lose some of its mass, mainly as water, before being transferred and packed closely into the silo. The container can be in the form of a pit, in clamps, towers or now often in big polythene bales. The fermentation to lactic acid is due mainly to species of *Lactobacillus* and *Enterococcus*, which are already present amongst the microflora on the harvested grass. Respiration of the plant material continues even after cutting, using up available oxygen. Provided the silo is well sealed, say with a polythene cover weighted down, conditions soon become anaerobic which encourages the activity of the lactic acid bacteria. While the plant material is actively respiring, there is some reduction in sugar content, which means loss of food reserves for feeding. Temperatures may rise inside the silo, but provided the rise is not excessive, the warmth encourages the fermentation processes. As lactic acid is produced, the pH falls, to between 4.2 and 3.8. By this time, the grass has been converted to silage, which is light yellow-brown in colour, has a sharp acid taste, little smell and if kept in suitable conditions is stable for several years.

As well as the bacteria which produce lactic acid, other undesirable bacteria are present which may affect the progress of ensiling. In particular, under cold and wet conditions, with low sugar availability, anaerobic species of *Clostridium* convert sugars and lactic acid to **butyric acid**. This results in a rancid smell and silage which is unpalatable to cattle. In addition, species of *Enterobacillus* convert sugars to **acetic acid**. Butyric and acetic acids are less effective in lowering the pH, so it takes longer for the pH to fall to 4.0 and more energy is lost in the process which means less carbohydrate for feeding the animal stock. Both *Clostridium* and *Enterobacillus* convert proteins to **ammonia**, which is alkaline, and thus raises the pH, so even more sugars must be broken down to achieve the desired pH. If the silage is exposed to air, aerobic species may oxidise carbohydrate material to carbon dioxide and water.

The quality of silage depends partly on the initial mixture of grass or other herbage and also on the conditions under which it is grown and harvested. To get the best silage during processing, the low pH should be reached quickly with minimum loss of carbohydrate reserve. Various procedures including the use of **additives** are adopted by farmers to help achieve this. Generally these aim to encourage the desirable anaerobic bacteria at the expense of the undesirable. The sugar content of the crop should be high at the time of harvest. This can be improved by selection of suitable grasses and by harvesting after midday and in sunny weather. The process of **wilting** helps reduce the quantity of material to be pickled so less lactic acid need be produced. **Cutting and bruising** the crop helps to release the cell contents and encourages rapid lactic acid production. The cut grass should be as clean as possible to avoid contamination by *Clostridia* and other species which are present in soil. Sugar in the form of **molasses** is often supplied as a means of increasing the water soluble carbohydrate available for the bacterial population (*Lactobacillus*) while ensiling progresses. The liquid molasses can be added by spraying to ensure good mixing with the silage material. **Enzymes** such as cellulases and hemicellulases are used to break down cellulosic material and so increase the available soluble carbohydrate. Addition of **preservatives** (such as formalin) with or without **acid** (such as formic acid) inhibits activity of

QUESTION

Why is cutting of grass for silage usually done after midday and why is it best to cut for silage on sunny rather than on cloudy days? Cutting and bruising of the grass helps to release juices and increases silage density. How does consolidation and dense packing of the silo affect the silage processing?
A commercially produced inoculant supplied to farmers had the following description: *Lactobacillus plantarum*, *Pediococcus acidilactici*, *Streptococcus faecium*, *Lactococcus lactis lactis*, Clostridial bacteriophages, hemicellulase and cellulase enzymes.
Suggest the likely benefit of each of these in making good quality silage.

USE OF MICROORGANISMS IN BIOTECHNOLOGY

Clostridia species and provides a suitable pH for the *Lactobacillus*. Increasingly, **inoculants** of desirable species of bacteria, particularly *Lactobacillus* and *Streptococcus*, are applied to the silage to ensure rapid fermentation to lactic acid.

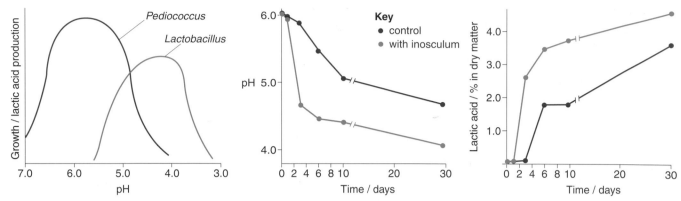

Figure 3.32 (a) Making silage – different bacteria contribute to production of lactic acid and lowering of the pH in fermentation to produce silage. The action of natural microbes can be enhanced by adding microbial inoculants of suitable bacteria; (b) The effect of inoculants on the rate of lactic acid production and pH change in silage made from vetch

Figure 3.33 (a) a typical pit for making silage. Note the black polythene cover (pulled aside) which is weighted down with tyres; (b) cattle being fed on silage.

Rhizobium and nodulation

The ability shown by certain bacteria and cyanobacteria to **fix nitrogen** is a fundamental stage in the natural recycling of nitrogen, and plays a significant part in the ecology of soil. Some nitrogen-fixing organisms are **free living** in the soil or water (such as species of *Azotobacter*), but many form specific **mutualistic associations** with roots or stems of plants, notably with the bacterial genus *Rhizobium*. Of considerable importance in agriculture are members of the family Papilionaceae (also known as Leguminosae or legumes) which include economically important crops such as alfalfa, clover, beans, peas, lucerne and soya beans. These leguminous plants are stimulated to form **root nodules** with *Rhizobium*. This nitrogen fixation leads to enhancement of the combined nitrogen in the plant material thus giving better yields of the crop (see *The Organism and the Environment*, 2nd edition, page 41). The ability to fix nitrogen can also be an advantage when growing crops on nitrogen-deficient soils.

The legume plant and bacterium can fix nitrogen only in this symbiotic association – neither can do so alone. It has been found that nodulation of the roots of the legume crop can be encouraged if an inoculum of an appropriate strain of *Rhizobium* is applied at the time seeds are sown. This can be done either by mixing the *Rhizobium* inoculum into a watery slurry with peat and applying this the same day that the seeds are sown or by incorporating the *Rhizobium* into pellets with the seeds. This is done before sowing and seeds treated this way can retain viability of the bacteria for several weeks or months if stored under suitable conditions. *Rhizobium* inoculants can be valuable, for example, in areas where a legume crop is being newly introduced or where *Rhizobium* is low in the soil.

Figure 3.34 Root nodules on roots of the runner bean, Phaseolus multiflorus, containing Rhizobium.

Microbes for biological control

Biological control of pests exploits interactions between organisms and implies the deliberate introduction of one species to control another (the pest). (See *The Organism and the Environment*, 2nd edition, Chapter 7.) Microbial pathogens can thus be exploited as biological control agents, and success has been achieved using bacteria, fungi and viruses. The term **microbial insecticide** is used when the **microorganism** is used to control insects, and the term **mycoherbicide** when pathogenic fungi are used to control weeds. While only a few mycoherbicides are currently being used commercially, it is an area where further research may be successful in providing alternatives to chemical herbicides for weed control.

A well established example of a microbial insecticide is *Bacillus thuringiensis*. This bacterium produces a glycoprotein, known as Bt, which is toxic to a variety of insects, such as butterflies, moths and beetles, but not to animals and humans. When ingested by the insect larvae, the toxin leads to paralysis or degeneration of the gut. The insect is usually killed within a few hours. Different bacterial subspecies produce toxins which are active against different insects, so the control can, to some extent, be species specific. Successful fungal insecticides, used on commercial crops, include *Verticillium lecanii*, applied in glasshouses to control aphids on chrysanthemums and whitefly on cucumbers.

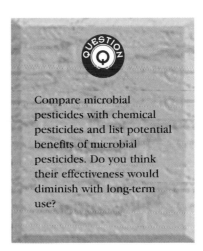

Compare microbial pesticides with chemical pesticides and list potential benefits of microbial pesticides. Do you think their effectiveness would diminish with long-term use?

Gene (DNA) technology and crop plants

The techniques of genetic modification are now being applied to the breeding of crop plants. For centuries, farmers have modified their plant crops and their domesticated animals. They have done this by the slow processes of breeding and selection of desired characteristics in the progeny and have thereby manipulated the gene pool and achieved considerable improvement in the varieties used. Examples of such improvements include increased yields and refinement of texture or flavour. Modern wheat grown for bread yields far more usable grain than the ancestral types. Animals have become more docile and the fat content of meat and milk has been reduced. Modern biotechnology carries conventional methods of breeding and artificial selection a stage further. With its 'cut and paste' techniques, DNA technology (gene technology) allows much more precise control of the specific genes that are incorporated into the genome and success is likely to be achieved in a much shorter time. Some of the aims in current research programmes are outlined in Table 3.9. The few examples of genetically modified (GM) crops given below illustrate a selection of the achievements up to 1997, though in this active field of research, the scene changes fast. The story behind **genetically modified tomatoes** is included to illustrate how the benefits of gene technology can directly affect consumers and their choice on the supermarket shelf.

Table 3.9 *Current research with genetically modified crop plants and possible benefits*

Feature in genetically modified organism	Possible benefits
improve efficiency of uptake of mineral salts	reduced fertiliser input
improve ability to withstand drought or high salt	crop can be cultivated on land where soil or climate is unsuitable
improve resistance to herbicides	crop better able to survive application of herbicides to control weeds
improve resistance to disease	reduced pesticide input, crop losses reduced
improve frost resistance	growing and harvest season extended
control ripening of fruits	postharvest losses reduced

Soya and herbicide resistance

Processed soya beans are used in many foods, to provide protein, oil and other ingredients. Varieties of genetically modified soya have been developed which are more tolerant of certain herbicides. The herbicides used break down relatively quickly in the soil into harmless components. The processed GM soya is indistinguishable from conventional soya in its composition and processing characteristics.

Maize and resistance to pests

Maize is used for both human and animal food and may be processed to provide flour, oil, syrups or other food ingredients. The European Corn Borer (ECB) is an insect pest which destroys around 4 per cent of maize crops on a global scale and up to 20 per cent in some regions. The pest causes damage by boring through the stem and ear of the maize plant, which then falls over. Genetically modified maize has been produced which shows resistance to pests. The pest-resistant maize produces a lethal protein when attacked by the insect. The gene for this toxic protein comes from *Bacillus thuringiensis*, which is already used widely in biological control. This protein is toxic to a variety of insects but not to animals or humans.

Rice and resistance to disease

Rice is a very important crop on a global scale, but suffers from the rice stripe virus (RSV). Transgenic rice, produced by introducing the gene for the virus protein coat into the rice plant genome, shows noticeably increased resistance to the rice stripe virus.

Genetically modified tomatoes

There is something both irresistible and alluring about a freshly picked, ripe home-grown tomato. The characteristic smell, texture and rich, sweet flavour, whether eaten raw or cooked to a simple sauce, are rarely experienced in mass produced supermarket tomatoes. This is hardly surprising. Commercial tomato growers are geared to large-scale production. The priorities are to maximise yield and minimise losses through disease. Production and harvest time are geared to consumer demand. The tomatoes are expected to be uniform in size and to arrive undamaged on the supermarket shelf. Flavour is not always high on the list of priorities. Often tomatoes are picked when they are green and unripe which means they are firm enough to survive the handling during harvesting, storage and distribution. To some extent the ripening stages can be controlled, so that pre-packed boxes of red tomatoes reach the supermarket shelves when required.

Tomatoes soften as they ripen mainly because of the activity of the enzyme polygalacturonase (PG). PG acts on pectic substances in the middle lamella within the cell wall structure, hydrolysing long polymers and converting them to shorter, more soluble fragments. The cells lose their cohesion, so begin to move in relation to each other. Turgor of the cells diminishes as the cell walls weaken, resulting in loss of firmness. Synthesis of PG coincides with a rise in ethene concentration and ethene is involved in promoting the ripening process. Inhibition of PG activity slows the softening but still allows development of the desirable flavours and colour associated with ripening.

Genetic modification, using two different methods, has led to a precise way of reducing the expression of the PG gene so that the tomato remains firm. The gene that codes for PG has been identified and sequenced. Using *Agrobacterium* as a vector, an 'antisense' PG gene has been inserted into the tomato plant (see Figure 3.37). An antisense gene is effectively a reversed form of the gene and is inherited in a normal Mendelian way. Transgenic tomatoes produced by antisense technology have been approved for sale in the USA, under the name of '*Flavr-Savr*'. However, production of Flavr-Savr tomatoes was short-lived, due to problems with disease resistance and harvesting. Research in the UK has produced genetically modified tomatoes with a shortened PG gene (Figure 3.33). In the UK, approval for the sale of paste (but not the fresh fruit) made from these genetically modified tomatoes was given in 1995.

As well as improved flavour, these tomatoes show improvements in consistency and viscosity, giving a thicker tomato paste, without the need for addition of thickeners. There is much less wastage in the field at harvest and in the processing. It is of interest that in one supermarket chain in the UK, over three quarters of a million cans of GM tomato paste were sold between its introduction in February 1996, up to November 1997. The cans were clearly labelled to indicate the paste had been made with GM tomatoes and the conventional equivalent was always available alongside. In some stores, sales of the GM paste exceeded that of the conventional paste.

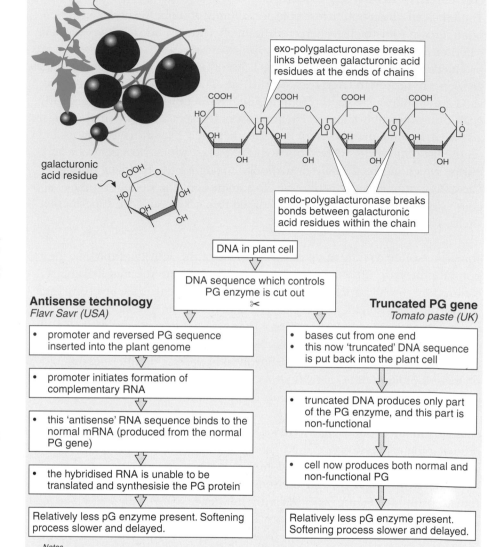

exo-polygalacturonase breaks links between galacturonic acid residues at the ends of chains

galacturonic acid residue

endo-polygalacturonase breaks bonds between galacturonic acid residues within the chain

DNA in plant cell

DNA sequence which controls PG enzyme is cut out

Antisense technology
Flavr Savr (USA)

Truncated PG gene
Tomato paste (UK)

- promoter and reversed PG sequence inserted into the plant genome

- bases cut from one end
- this now 'truncated' DNA sequence is put back into the plant cell

- promoter initiates formation of complementary RNA

- truncated DNA produces only part of the PG enzyme, and this part is non-functional

- this 'antisense' RNA sequence binds to the normal mRNA (produced from the normal PG gene)

- cell now produces both normal and non-functional PG

- the hybridised RNA is unable to be translated and synthesisie the PG protein

Relatively less pG enzyme present. Softening process slower and delayed.

Relatively less pG enzyme present. Softening process slower and delayed.

Notes

1 **Antisense technology** - A normal functioning gene produces a message which makes 'sense'. The 'promoter' is a DNA sequence at the beginning of the gene which promotes transcription of the gene, producing the mRNA from the DNA strand. Antisense technology inserts the promoter and the sequence of DNA into the genome of the plant cell, but at a different position and reserves the orientation. This DNA sequence now produces 'antisense' mRNA which is complementary to the normal sense RNA. These complementary strands of RNA bind together, so making the mRNA non-functional in terms of synthesising the relevant protein.

2 You will see that no 'foreign' DNA has been introduced into the tomatoes. In both methods, the genetic modification has been achieved by manipulation of the tomato plant's own DNA.

Figure 3.37 Two routes to genetically modified tomatoes

Figure 3.36 (a) Tomatoes on sale in a supermarket; (b) tomato paste from genetically modified tomatoes, on sale in the UK; (c) a basketful of homegrown tomatoes - rich red in colour, variable in size and shape and picked when ripe, ready to eat and full of flavour.

The benefits of DNA technology in crop plants can be viewed in a wider context. Increased resistance to disease reduces crop losses but there are additional environmental as well as economic benefits through reducing dependence on chemical pesticides. Slower or controlled ripening of fruits, or firmer but ripe tomatoes, means better quality for the consumer, as well as reduced postharvest crop losses. Improved frost resistance in strawberries could extend the growing season and hence the availability of fresh produce for the consumer. The possibilities of applying DNA technology and tapping of genetic resources could have a greater impact than the so-called Green Revolution of the 1960s and 1970s, which relied upon the intensive input of fertilisers, pesticides and herbicides. In the face of escalating world population, biotechnology gives considerable hope to people in developing countries to overcome the shortfall in food production.

Do you think that herbicide-resistant crop plants would encourage more or less use of herbicides?

What benefits might there be if the ability to fix nitrogen was transferred to cereal crops? Think about the economics, possibility of growing crops on marginal land, and environmental consequences in relation to use of fertilisers.

Compare the influence that biotechnology could have on crop production with the energy inputs of intensive farming methods. Make a case that biotechnology could help small-scale subsistence farmers in poor agricultural areas. Then list some of the worries that biotechnology would just increase profits for large multinational companies in agriculture and in the food industry.

DNA (gene) technology and some ethical considerations

DNA technology provides a means of introducing precise and controlled genetic change, offering opportunities for improvements in agriculture, the food industry and medical therapy. DNA technology can also be exploited as a detective tool – diagnosing genetic defects, in forensic work and to trace patterns of relatedness between individuals or species.

Some people oppose the use of DNA technology because they feel it interferes with natural processes and that genetically modified organisms (GMOs) could be harmful to humans or to the environment. Generally people are more willing to accept DNA technology when applied to the field of medicine or involving plants but more cautious when it is applied to food or farm animals.

List some of the arguments for and against the use of DNA technology. How could you explain simply, to a non-scientist, the basic steps involved in DNA technology?

Give an indication of any safeguards you know are taken, or you think should be taken, when doing research with GMOs and in the release of GMOs.

For centuries people have eaten rice from plants infected with RSV (rice stripe virus; see page 66). Do you think the same people would be happy to eat transgenic rice which contains the gene for the virus protein coat?

How should information about GM foods be presented to the public? Do you think that all products which contain GMOs or GM derived food should be labelled, or should the labelling be applied to all products which do not contain GM foods? How, in practical terms, would a labelling directive be implemented? What information would you give on the label?

Preparation and sterilisation of media

Introduction

There are many different types of media which are used for the culture of microorganisms. These may be obtained in ready formulated preparations, or can be made up using separate ingredients. In this practical, we look at the method for preparing and sterilising two different media: **nutrient broth**, which can be used for the culture of bacteria, and **malt extract agar**, which is used for the culture of fungi, such as *Penicillium*. If you are using ready-formulated media, follow the manufacturer's instructions carefully, and make up the media using distilled water.

Materials for nutrient broth

- Beef extract   1.0 g
- Yeast extract   2.0 g
- Peptone   5.0 g
- Sodium chloride   5.0 g
- Distilled water   1 dm^3
  pH 7.4 (approximately)

Method

Add the beef extract, peptone and sodium chloride to the water, heat gently and mix continuously until the ingredients are dissolved. If a solid medium is required (nutrient agar) add 15 g of agar powder to the ingredients and stir until dissolved. Dispense into suitable containers and autoclave at 121 °C for 15 minutes. If using fire agar powder be careful not to inhale any. If using prepared medium tablets, add 1 tablet to 5 cm^3 of distilled water and soak for 15 minutes. Sterilise by autoclaving at 121 °C for 15 minutes. Make sure you are familiar with safe use of the autoclave before doing this.

Materials for malt extract agar

- Malt extract   30.0 g
- Mycological peptone   5.0 g
- Agar powder   15.0 g
- Distilled water   1 dm^3
  pH 5.4 (approximately)

Add the ingredients to 1 dm^3 of distilled water and leave to soak for 15 minutes.

Dispense into suitable containers and sterilise by autoclaving at 115 °C for 10 minutes. If using prepared medium tablets, add 1 tablet to 5 cm^3 of distilled water and sterilise by autoclaving at 115 °C for 10 minutes.

When autoclaving screw-capped containers, remember to loosen the lids slightly to allow for expansion of air inside the containers. Tighten the lids again after autoclaving, when the containers have cooled.

Preparation of a heat-fixed smear of bacteria

Introduction

Before staining bacteria with crystal violet, or using the Gram's stain, it is necessary to prepare a heat-fixed smear. This can be stained simply with a solution of crystal violet to see the cells clearly, or stained using Gram's method to distinguish between Gram positive and Gram negative cells.

Materials

- Clean, grease-free microscope slides. Microscope slides should be kept in 70% (aqueous) Industrial Methylated Spirit (IMS) and wiped dry immediately before use. Keep away from naked flames.
- Freshly-grown broth or plate culture of a suitable bacterium such as *Bacillus subtilis*
- Inoculating loop
- Bunsen burner
- Small bottle of sterile distilled water
- Crystal violet stain
- Discard jar containing disinfectant

industr
methyla
spirit
HIGHI
FLAMMA

Method

1 Flame the loop, then transfer a drop of sterile distilled water to the centre of a clean microscope slide.
2 Flame the loop again, then transfer a small drop of the culture to the distilled water on the slide and mix carefully using the loop. Spread the mixture outwards to produce a thin, oval film on the slide. Flame the loop.

3 Dry the film well above, or near, a Bunsen flame. DO NOT ALLOW THE SLIDE TO STEAM.

4 When the film has dried, pass the slide quickly two or three times through the flame to heat-fix.

5 The film can now be stained.

6 After staining and examination using a microscope, the slide should be discarded into disinfectant or an autoclave.

The Gram Stain

Introduction

The Gram stain (first developed in 1884 by Christian Gram) is a very important technique used in the identification of bacteria. On the basis of this technique, bacteria can be divided into two groups, **Gram positive** or **Gram negative**. There are major differences between the structures of the cell walls of these two groups. Gram positive organisms retain a crystal violet-iodine complex and appear purple, whereas Gram negative organisms will be decolorised by organic solvents. The cells are then counterstained using, for example, safranin. Gram negative cells appear red or pink. For reliable results, it is important to use freshly growing cultures of bacteria. Gram positive bacteria include *Lactobacillus*, *Bacillus* and the majority of cocci, such as *Staphylococcus*. Gram negative bacteria include *Escherichia coli* (*E. coli*), *Salmonella* and some cocci.

Materials

- Freshly growing broth culture or plate culture of suitable bacteria, such as *Bacillus subtilis*, *Lactobacillus*, or *Escherichia coli*
- Clean, grease-free microscope slides. Slides should be kept in 70% (aqueous) Industrial Methylated Spirit (IMS) and wiped dry immediately before use. Keep away from naked flames
- Inoculating loop
- Small bottle of sterile distilled water
- Crystal violet stain (dissolve 2 g of crystal violet in 100 cm³ of absolute alcohol. Make up a second solution containing 1 g

of ammonium oxalate in 100 cm³ of distilled water. Add 25 cm³ of the crystal violet solution to 100 cm³ of ammonium oxalate solution.)

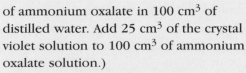
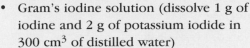

- Gram's iodine solution (dissolve 1 g of iodine and 2 g of potassium iodide in 300 cm³ of distilled water)
- Alcohol – 70% (aqueous) IMS to decolorise stained smear. Keep away from naked flames
- 1% (aqueous) safranin solution
- Bunsen burner
- Microscope fitted with oil immersion objective
- Immersion oil
- Discard jar containing disinfectant

Method

1 Prepare a **heat-fixed smear** of bacteria on a clean, grease-free microscope slide.

2 Place the slide on staining bars over a sink and flood the slide with **crystal violet solution**. Leave for 30 seconds then rinse with tap water.

3 Cover the film with **iodine solution**. Leave for 30 seconds, then rinse off the iodine solution with tap water.

4 Rinse the slide with **alcohol**, until the washings are pale violet. Be careful not to over-decolorise

5 Rinse with tap water, then counterstain using **safranin**.

6 Finally, rinse the slide with tap water and gently blot dry.

7 Examine using oil immersion.

Results and further work

1 Compare the appearance of Gram positive and Gram negative bacterial cells

2 Find out about the importance of the Gram's stain in relation to the use of antibiotics.

Preparation of a streak plate of bacteria

Introduction

In this practical, an agar plate will be poured using sterile nutrient agar and inoculated using a culture of a suitable bacterium, such as *Bacillus subtilis*. Streak plates are useful to isolate pure cultures, as individual

colonies will have grown from a single cell. Single colonies can be used to subculture another sterile agar plate to obtain a pure isolate.

Materials

- Sterile Petri dishes
- Sterile nutrient agar
- Boiling water bath
- Bacteriological loop
- Slope culture of *Bacillus subtilis*, or other suitable bacterium
- Chinagraph pencil, or spirit marker pen

Method – pouring a sterile agar plate

1 Before starting, wipe the bench surface using a suitable disinfectant solution.

2 Melt the agar in a boiling water bath, remove carefully using tongs and allow to cool to about 45 °C. At this temperature, the agar will be cool enough to handle safely, but will remain molten. Agar starts to set below about 42 °C.

3 On the <u>base</u> of a sterile Petri dish, write your name, the date, and the name of the organism with which the plate will be inoculated. Petri dishes should always be labelled on the base, as it is possible for lids to be transposed.

4 Working near a Bunsen burner with a blue flame, hold the bottle of molten, but cooled, nutrient agar in one hand and, using your little finger of the other hand, remove the lid of the bottle. Do not place the lid on the bench.

5 Pass the neck of the bottle through the Bunsen flame then, using the hand in which you are holding the lid of the bottle, raise the lid of the Petri dish to an angle of about 45° and carefully pour in the agar until he dish is nearly half full. Replace the Petri dish lid, flame the neck of the bottle again and replace the lid.

6 Leave the agar plate to set.

Method – preparing a streak plate

1 Have ready your sterile agar plate and a slope culture of the bacterium to be used.

2 Sterilise the bacteriological loop by holding it in a blue bunsen flame until red hot.

3 Allow the loop to cool and, whilst still holding the loop, remove the lid from the slope culture using the little finger of the hand in which you are holding the loop. Do not place the lid on the bench.

4 Pass the neck of the culture bottle through the bunsen flame, then use the loop to remove a small portion of the culture. Replace the lid on the culture bottle.

5 Now lift the lid of the Petri dish and use the loop to streak out the culture as shown in Figure P.1. Be careful not to 'plough up' the surface of the agar. When you have finished, flame the loop again before placing it on the bench.

6 Fasten the lid of the Petri dish using two pieces of adhesive tape. Invert the dish, and incubate at 30 °C for 24 hours.

Results and discussion

1 Record the appearance of your streak plate after incubation. Were you successful in obtaining single colonies of the bacterium?

2 List the different methods of sterilisation which have been used in this practical.

3 Explain why is it important:
   (a) to avoid ploughing up the surface of the agar when inoculating
   (b) not seal the dishes all the way round with adhesive tape, and
   (c) to invert the dishes when they are incubated.

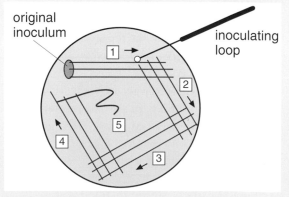

Figure P.1 Preparing a streak plate. Streak in the directions shown by the arrows. The loop should be flamed and allowed to cool between each set of three streaks

Use of pipettes and spreaders

For quantitative work, it may be necessary to inoculate an agar plate with a known volume of inoculum, for example, a culture of microorganisms growing in a broth medium, or a milk sample, to enumerate the bacteria present. For this purpose, a sterile pipette is used to transfer say 0.1 cm³ of the inoculum to the surface of the agar. The inoculum is then spread evenly over the surface of the agar using a sterile glass spreader. After incubation, the number of colonies can be counted – we know that this represents the number of viable cells originally present in the volume of inoculum used.

Pasteur pipettes, previously plugged with a small piece of cotton wool and sterilised by autoclaving, can be attached to a 1.0 cm³ plastic syringe (insulin syringes, with the needle removed, are ideal for this purpose) by means of a piece of silicone rubber tubing. After use, the pipette should be placed in a discard jar containing disinfectant. Glass spreaders can be made from glass rod. These should be sterilised immediately prior to use by dipping in a beaker containing a small volume of Industrial Methylated Spirit (IMS), then passing the spreader through a Bunsen flame and allowing the alcohol to burn off. After use, the spreader should be placed in a discard jar of disinfectant. Remember to keep the beaker of IMS well away from the Bunsen flame. If the IMS in the beaker should ignite, cover with a wet cloth. An alternative, avoiding ethanol, is to use cotton wool swabs, wrapped in foil and pre-sterilised by autoclaving.

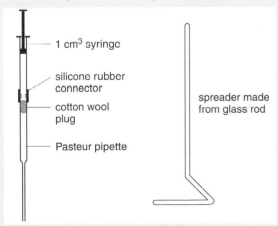

1 cm³ syringe

silicone rubber connector

cotton wool plug

Pasteur pipette

spreader made from glass rod

Figure P.2 A pipette and glass spreader

Use of different carbon sources for growth
Introduction

The purpose of this practical is to investigate the ability of yeast to utilise different carbon sources as substrates for respiration. A range of different carbohydrates is used as carbon sources and relative rates of respiration will be determined by measuring the production of acid by the yeast cells: the faster the rate of respiration, the faster the rate of acid production.

Materials

- 2% (aqueous) solutions of the following sugars: glucose, fructose, galactose, sucrose, lactose, maltose
- Top pan balance
- Dried yeast granules
- Seven 500 cm³ flasks, with cotton wool plugs
- Ammonium phosphate and ammonium sulphate
- Incubator, or water bath set at 25 °C
- Burette and stand
- 0.1 mol per dm³ sodium hydroxide solution
- Conical flasks for titration
- 25 cm³ volumetric pipette and filler
- Phenolphthalein indicator solution

WEAR EYE PROTECTION

sodium hydroxide solution IRRITANT

Method

1. Add 200 cm³ of each sugar solution to separate, appropriately labelled flasks. Include one flask containing 200 cm³ of distilled water as a control.
2. Add 2 g of dried yeast and 1 g of culture nutrients to each flask. The culture nutrients are a mixture of equal masses of ammonium phosphate and ammonium sulphate. Swirl the flasks, or stir thoroughly with a glass rod, to ensure that the nutrients dissolve and that the yeast is resuspended.
3. Plug each flask with cotton wool and incubate overnight at 25 °C.
4. Set up a burette containing 0.1 mol per dm³ sodium hydroxide solution.
5. After incubation, swirl each flask thoroughly to mix the contents and remove a 25 cm³ sample of each

culture. Place each sample in separate, labelled conical flasks. Add two or three drops of phenolphthalein indicator solution to each.

6 Titrate each sample against the sodium hydroxide solution to find the volume of alkali required to neutralise the acid produced by the yeast.

Results and discussion

1 Record your results in a table. Include class results for titrations, or duplicate your own titrations.

2 Plot a bar graph to show the volume of alkali required to neutralise the acid produced by yeast in each sugar solution.

3 From your results state which sugar produced
    (a) the fastest rate of respiration
    (b) the slowest rate of respiration.

4 Suggest how the relative rates of respiration may be linked to the growth rate of yeast in the different sugars. How could you extend this investigation to find the relative growth rate of yeast in the different sugars ?

Further work

This practical can be extended to investigate the effects of different nitrogen sources on the fermentation rate or growth rate of yeast. In the method above, nitrogen is provided in the form of ammonium ions, but you could investigate the effect of adding nitrogen to the medium in the forms of urea or as amino acids using casein hydrolysate.

The relationship between growth and nitrogen concentration can be investigated suitably using *Chlorella*, grown in an aerated mineral salts medium. Availability of nitrogen is then controlled by using KNO_3 in the range 1 to 10 mg per dm^3.

Counting cells using a haemocytometer

Introduction

A haemocytometer consists of a special glass slide with an accurately ruled etched grid of precise dimensions. Originally developed for counting blood cells, hence the name, the

haemocytometer can also be used for counting microorganisms in a liquid medium. It is particularly suitable for counting yeast or *Chlorella* cells, as these are readily visible and non-motile, but is not suitable for bacteria. Unless special staining techniques are used, it is not possible to distinguish between living and dead cells, therefore this method of counting, known as a **direct count**, gives the total number of cells including both living (or viable) and dead (non-viable) cells. There are several different types of haemocytometers: one which is frequently used is known as the **Improved Neubauer**. This has two counting grids, each of which consists of a central area measuring 1 mm × 1 mm, divided into 25 large squares. Each large square is edged by triple ruled lines and consists of 16 small squares. There are therefore **25 × 16 = 400 small squares** in the counting grid. When the coverslip is correctly positioned over the counting grid, the depth of the counting chamber is 0.1 mm, the volume over one small square is therefore 1/4000 mm^3. In practice, we usually count the number of cells present in 5 large squares, that is, 80 small squares, so to calculate the total number of cells present per mm^3, the following formula is used

number of cells per mm^3 = $\frac{N}{80} \times 4000$

where **N** is the number of cells counted in **80** small squares.

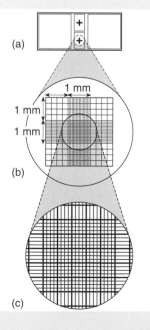

Figure P.3 The Improved Neubau haemocytometer, viewed at increasing magnifications: (a) × 0.4; (b) × 7; (c) × 23

To use the haemocytometer accurately, it is essential to set it up and fill the counting chamber carefully, otherwise gross errors will be introduced.

Materials

- Improved Neubauer haemocytometer and coverslip
- IMS and tissues to clean the haemocytometer
- Broth culture of suitable organism to count
- 1 cm³ syringe with needle
- Microscope

Method

1 Place the haemocytometer on a flat surface and thoroughly clean the slide and coverslip using alcohol.

2 Slide the coverslip into position using a firm, downward pressure. When correctly positioned, a rainbow pattern (Newton's rings) should be visible along the two edges of the coverslip where it is supported by the slide. Note: if you are using an ordinary thin coverslip, do not press downwards as this can bend the coverslip downwards and decrease the volume of the counting chamber.

3 Thoroughly mix the cell culture to ensure a homogeneous suspension and, using the syringe, carefully inject a sample of the culture under the coverslip. The culture must exactly fill the silvered part of the counting chamber, it MUST NOT overflow into the grooves on either side. If it does, the counting chamber must be cleaned and refilled.

4 Leave the haemocytometer for at least five minutes to allow the cells to settle onto the grid, then, using a low light intensity, carefully focus under the low power of the microscope to locate the grid. When the grid is in focus, increase the magnification to × 400.

5 Count the number of cells present in 5 large squares (80 small squares), using the pattern shown in Figure P.4. Some

cells will lie on the boundaries between large squares, that is, touching the triple lines. To ensure a consistent counting method, count only those cells which touch the central line on the north and west sides of the square. Those cells touching the central line on the south and east sides should be ignored.

6 If there are too many cells to count, an accurate dilution, such as 1 in 100, should be made and your final count should then be multiplied by the dilution factor.

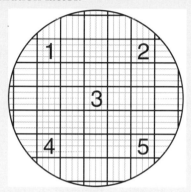

Figure P.4 Count the total number of cells in these five triple-lined squares. What are the dimensions of each triple-lined square?

Counting cells using the pour plate dilution method

Introduction

Using a haemocytometer gives a direct, total count of the number of cells present in a suspension. The pour plate dilution method will count only viable cells and relies on the ability of each single viable cell to grow and produce a visible colony on an agar plate. The number of colonies will therefore correspond to the number of viable cells which were originally present in the sample. However, it is likely that the original sample will contain far too many cells to count accurately and therefore we make an accurate series of dilutions. Samples of each dilution are then plated out and the number of colonies counted in a suitable dilution. The number of viable cells originally present in the sample is then found by multiplying the number of colonies by the dilution factor.

PRACTICAL

Materials

- Six universal bottles or similar, capped containers, each containing 9 cm^3 of sterile distilled water
- Six sterile Pasteur pipettes, plugged with cotton wool
- Six sterile Petri dishes
- Suitable culture for counting, such as a sample of pasteurised milk.
- Supply of suitable sterile medium, molten, kept in a water bath at 45 °C. China blue lactose agar is ideal for counting the number of bacteria present in a sample of milk.
- 1 cm^3 plastic syringe, fitted with silicone rubber connector, to attach to Pasteur pipettes
- Bunsen burner
- Chinagraph or spirit marker pen
- Discard jar containing disinfectant
- Incubator at 30 °C.

Method

1 Look carefully at the flow chart (Figure P.5) for this experiment and ensure that you have the necessary materials to hand. Label the containers of sterile distilled water 10^{-1}, 10^{-2}, 10^{-3}, 10^{-4}, 10^{-5} and 10^{-6}, and the six Petri dishes similarly. Remember to label the Petri dishes on their bases.

2 Shake the sample thoroughly to ensure that it is uniformly mixed then, using aseptic technique, transfer 1.0 cm^3 to the container labelled 10^{-1}. Use a sterile Pasteur pipette fitted with a plastic syringe. After use, discard the pipette into a jar of disinfectant. Mix this dilution carefully then, using a fresh

sterile pipette, transfer 1.0 cm^3 to the container labelled 10^{-2}. Continue in this way until you have completed the dilution series.

3 Using a fresh, sterile pipette each time transfer a 1.0 cm^3 sample of each dilution separately to the appropriately labelled Petri dishes.

4 Again using aseptic technique, carefully pour molten, but cooled, sterile agar medium into each Petri dish. Swirl very carefully to ensure that the sample and agar are thoroughly mixed. Moving the dish gently in a figure-of-eight pattern on the bench will ensure mixing, but DO NOT allow the agar to spill over the edge of the dishes.

5 Allow the agar to set, then fasten each lid with two pieces of adhesive tape.

6 Invert the dishes and incubate at 30 °C.

Results and discussion

1 After incubation, count the number of colonies in a dish containing a suitable dilution.

2 Calculate the number of viable cells originally present in 1.0 cm^3 of the sample.

3 What are the possible sources of error in this method?

Other methods for measuring the growth of microorganisms

The growth of microorganisms in a broth medium can be measured using optical methods. These rely on the fact that as the number of microorganisms increases, the medium will become more cloudy, or turbid. The turbidity of the medium is therefore

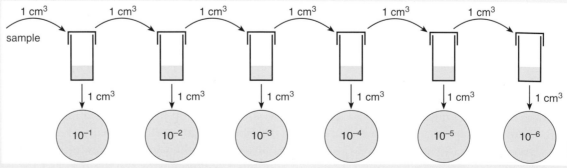

Figure P.5 Flow chart for the pour plate dilution method

related to the total number of cells in the culture. The turbidity of a cell suspension is measured using an instrument known as a nephelometer, which actually measures the light which is scattered by the cells when a beam of light is passed through the cell suspension.

A colorimeter can be used to measure the light absorbance of a cell suspension; as the number of cells increases, the light absorbance will also increase. This method provides a simple means of measuring cell growth and can be used to provide rapid results by taking samples from a broth medium while the culture is growing. If used with a rapidly growing microorganism, such as *Beneckea natriegens* (*Vibrio natriegens*), a growth curve can be obtained within about 3 hours.

A colorimeter is also suitable for monitoring the growth of *Chlorella* in a liquid medium. Samples can be removed on a daily basis from a culture growing in an aerated mineral salts medium, in a 500 cm³ or 1 dm³ flask, and the absorbance of each sample measured at either 410 nm or 665 nm. For further work, the relationship between absorbance and cell counts, using a haemocytometer, can be investigated.

To measure the biomass of a large-scale culture of an organism such as *Chlorella*, or *Saccharomyces*, the cells should be removed by filtration and dried to constant mass, which is then recorded.

Investigation of yoghurt production

Introduction

In this practical, we investigate some of the factors which affect the production of yoghurt. Bacteria in the starter culture ferment milk sugars to produce organic acids, such as methanoic and lactic acid, and consequently the pH will fall. The rate of change in pH can be used to indicate the rate of formation of yoghurt.

Materials

- UHT milk
- Natural yoghurt to use as a starter culture

- Boiling tubes
- Pipettes or syringes
- Cling film
- Glass stirring rod
- pH meter (if unavailable, narrow range pH papers could be used as an alternative)
- Water bath at 43 °C

Method

1 Transfer 10.0 cm³ of UHT milk into a boiling tube then add 1.0 cm³ of natural yoghurt.
2 Record the pH of the mixture, cover the tube with cling film, and incubate in a water bath at 43 °C.
3 Record the pH and changes in the appearance of the yoghurt at intervals of 30 minutes for up to 5 hours.

Results and discussion

1 Record your results in a table, then plot a graph to show changes in the pH during fermentation.
2 Describe the changes which occurred in pH and in the appearance of the yoghurt during fermentation.
3 Prepare a flow chart to show the stages in industrial yoghurt manufacture.

Further work

1 Investigate the effect of temperature on the rate of formation of yoghurt, by repeating the experiment at, for example, 20 °C, 30 °C, 40 °C and 50 °C.
2 Investigate the changes in pH during production of yoghurt using different types of milk, such as that from a cow, goat or sheep.
3 Investigate changes in pH during production of yoghurt using lactose reduced milk, such as Lactolite, or starter cultures containing *Lactobacillus acidophilus* and *Bifidobacterium bifidum*.
4 Devise a method to investigate changes in reducing sugar content during the production of yoghurt.
5 The relative viscosity of the final product can be measured by determining the

SAFETY NOTE:
Food made in a laboratory **MUST NOT** be tasted.

time taken for a sample of the yoghurt to pass through a funnel, such as a filter funnel. This is the principle of a viscometer.

6 Devise an experiment to investigate factors affecting the rate of fermentation of sucrose solution by *Saccharomyces cerevisiae*. A simple way of measuring the rate of fermentation is to measure changes in the specific gravity of the sugar and yeast mixture, using a hydrometer. The rate of anaerobic respiration can also be measured using a respirometer (see *Use of a simple respirometer* in *Systems and their Maintenance*). You could investigate the effects of factors such as:

- temperature
- pH of the medium. The pH can be adjusted by using 0.01 mol per dm³ citric acid monohydrate, or 0.1 mol per dm³ trisodium citrate dihydrate
- initial sucrose concentration (suggested range 0.25 to 2.0 mol per dm³)
- the effects of different substrates, such as sucrose, glucose, maltose and fructose using different strains of yeast.

Determination of bacterial sensitivity to antibiotics by agar diffusion

Introduction

The sensitivity of bacteria to particular antibiotics can be demonstrated using an agar diffusion technique. This method relies on the diffusion of the antibiotic from a small disc of filter paper, which has been impregnated with the antibiotic, into an agar medium which is seeded with the bacteria to be tested. The antibiotic will diffuse into the agar forming a circular area around the filter paper disc and, if the bacteria are sensitive to the antibiotic, they will be inhibited from growing in this area. A clear inhibition zone therefore develops around the disc if the bacteria are sensitive to the antibiotic. If the bacteria are resistant to the antibiotic, no inhibition zone will develop. The diameter of the inhibition zone is proportional to the concentration of a particular antibiotic; this

forms the basis of microbiological assay methods which are used to determine concentrations of antimicrobial substances present in, for example, plasma. Microbiological assay is a very sensitive method for detecting minute concentrations of substances, within the range of 2 to 8 μg per cm³, but the results must be interpreted with caution, as there are a number of factors which influence the size of the inhibition zone including:

- the concentration of the test substance
- the composition of the medium
- the depth of the medium
- the incubation temperature
- the test organism.

Materials

- Broth culture of suitable test organism, such as *Bacillus subtilis*
- Nutrient agar plates
- Discard jar containing disinfectant
- Glass beaker containing Industrial Methylated Spirit (IMS)
- Forceps
- Bunsen burner
- Oxoid multodisc or equivalent
- Incubator at 30 °C

industr
methyla
spirit
HIGHL
FLAMMA

Method

1 Use a sterile Pasteur pipette to flood the surface of a nutrient agar plate with broth culture of *Bacillus subtilis*. Rock the plate carefully so that the whole surface is covered with the broth.

2 Tip the excess broth into a solution of disinfectant and allow the plate to dry at 30 °C for half an hour.

3 Flame the forceps to sterilise, then place a multodisc on the surface of the agar, pressing down carefully. If you are using separate antibiotic sensitivity discs, up to six can be placed on one agar plate.

4 Flame the forceps again after use.

5 Allow the agar plate to stand at room temperature for 3 hours to allow the antibiotics to diffuse into the medium

6 Incubate the plate at 30 °C for 24 hours.

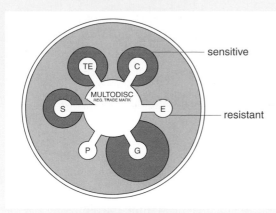

Figure P.6 Oxoid multodisc

Results and discussion

1 Record the appearance of your plate after incubation.

2 Record whether the test organism was sensitive or resistant to each antibiotic. If possible, compare the results of two different species of bacteria, such as *Escherichia coli* and *Bacillus subtilis*.

3 Why are sensitivity tests of clinical importance?

Note: It is important that the inhibition zones of each antibiotic are judged separately and not compared with each other. A larger inhibition zone does not necessarily mean that the test organism is more sensitive to that particular antibiotic.

Further work

The principle of this technique can be used to investigate the antimicrobial properties of disinfectants, toothpastes, mouthwashes, etc. Instead of placing filter paper discs on the surface of the agar, use a sterilised cork borer to remove cylindrical plugs of agar, seal the base of each well with a drop of agar and place one drop of the test solution, using a sterile Pasteur pipette, into each well.

Use of immobilised enzymes

Introduction

Immobilised enzymes have a wide range of commercial applications, such as their use in the production of lactose-reduced milk, using immobilised lactase (or β galactosidase). Immobilised enzymes are attached to inert, insoluble materials and have a number of advantages over enzymes in free solution, including the ability to reuse the enzyme, which reduces the overall cost of the process. Immobilised enzymes can also be used in continuous processes, which can be automated, and some enzymes are more stable when immobilised and are therefore less likely to be denatured. Enzymes can be immobilised in a range of materials, including agar gels, cellulose and polyacrylamide. The purpose of this practical is to produce immobilised lactase and to investigate its effect on lactose present in milk.

Materials

- 2 cm^3 lactase, e.g. Novo Nordisk Lactozym®
- 8 cm^3 of 2% sodium alginate solution, made up in distilled water. When making up the alginate solution, add the alginate slowly to warm distilled water and stir constantly
- 100 cm^3 of 2% calcium chloride solution in a plastic beaker
- Semi-quantitative glucose test strips, such as Diabur 5000
- Small piece of nylon gauze or muslin
- 10 cm^3 plastic syringe
- 10 cm^3 plastic syringe barrel
- Retort stand
- Short length of tubing, to fit plastic syringe, and screw clip
- 100 cm^3 beaker
- Glass rod
- Plastic tea strainer
- Distilled water
- Pasteurised milk

Method

1 Mix the sodium alginate solution with the enzyme solution in a beaker, then transfer to a plastic syringe.

2 Add this mixture drop-wise to the calcium chloride solution. Alginate beads, containing the immobilised enzyme, will form immediately. Leave to harden for 10 to 20 minutes.

3 Strain off the beads using the tea strainer and rinse with distilled water.

WEAR EYE
PROTECTION

4 Put a piece of nylon gauze in a 10 cm³ syringe barrel, to prevent the beads becoming stuck in the outlet, then add the beads to the syringe. Hold the syringe using a retort stand

5 Close the screw clip, then fill the syringe with milk. Open the clip slightly, and test the products for the presence of glucose. If you use quantitative test strips, such as Diabur 5000, you can investigate the relationship between time and glucose concentration.

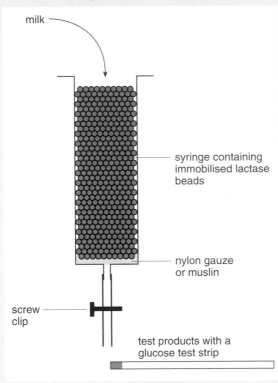

milk

syringe containing immobilised lactase beads

nylon gauze or muslin

screw clip

test products with a glucose test strip

Figure P.7 Use of immobilised enzymes

Further work – immobilised whole cells

Whole cells can be immobilised in a similar way to preparing immobilised enzymes, by entrapping them in alginate beads. Immobilised cells have a number of commercial applications, for example, in the industrial preparation of monoclonal antibodies using hybridoma cells encapsulated in calcium alginate beads. In this practical, yeast cells are immobilised in calcium alginate and used to hydrolyse sucrose into its constituent monosaccharides.

Materials

- 4% sodium alginate solution in distilled water
- 5 g of fresh yeast mixed with 100 cm³ of distilled water
- 100 cm³ of 1.5% calcium chloride solution in a plastic beaker
- 2% sucrose solution
- Glucose test strips, such as Diabur 5000
- Small piece of nylon gauze or muslin
- 10 cm³ plastic syringe
- 10 cm³ plastic syringe barrel
- Retort stand
- Short length of tubing, to fit syringe, and screw clip
- 100 cm³ beaker
- Glass rod
- Plastic tea strainer
- Distilled water

Method

1 Mix 5 cm³ of the sodium alginate solution with 5 cm³ of yeast suspension, then transfer the mixture to a plastic syringe.

2 Add this mixture drop-wise to the calcium chloride solution. Leave the alginate beads for 10 to 20 minutes to harden.

3 Strain off the beads and rinse with distilled water.

4 Put a piece of nylon gauze in a 10 cm³ syringe barrel, then add the beads. Hold the syringe using a retort stand.

5 Close the screw clip, then fill the syringe with 2 per cent sucrose solution. Open the clip slightly and test the products for the presence of glucose.

Suggestions for further work

Immobilised enzymes and whole cells offer a number of possibilities for individual studies. You could investigate the effect of bead diameter, or substrate flow rate on the rate of reactions. Investigate the ability of immobilised yeast cells to utilise a range of carbohydrates in a fermentation experiment. *Chlorella* cells can be immobilised and used to investigate the effects of mineral deficiencies on pigment synthesis.

Examination questions

Chapter 1

1 The table below refers to cell structure features of *Bacillus*, *Chlorella* and *Saccharomyces*.
   If the structure is present, place a tick (✔) in the appropriate box and is the structure is absent, place a cross (✘) in the appropriate box.

Structure	*Bacillus*	*Chlorella*	*Saccharomyces*
Cellulose cell wall			
Chloroplast			
Glycogen granules			
True nucleus			

(Total 4 marks)

2 The diagram below shows the structure of a typical bacterial cell as revealed by electron microscopy.

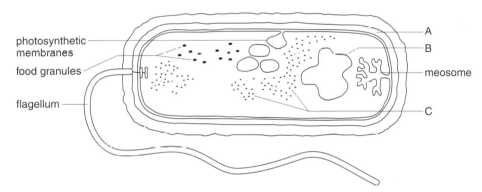

(a) Give *one* function of the structures labelled A, B and C. (3 marks)
(b) Gram staining can be used in the identification of bacteria.
   (i) Explain the difference in appearance after staining between a sample of Gram negative bacteria and a sample of Gram positive bacteria. (2 marks)
   (ii) Give *one* example of a genus of Gram negative bacteria.
   (1 mark)
   (Total 6 marks)

3 Read the following passage on Gram staining and then write on the dotted lines the most appropriate word or words to complete the account.

   Gram positive and Gram negative bacteria differ in their ability to keep a stain in their cell walls. A slide of bacteria is first flooded with a suitable stain such as .... All bacteria absorb this stain, which is then fixed with Gram's .... before being decolourised with .... Gram positive bacteria retain the stain complex, but Gram negative bacteria do not. Counterstaining with a red stain, such as .... causes Gram negative bacteria to absorb it and become red. Gram positive bacteria remain .... in colour.

(Total 5 marks)

4 *(a)* Describe the role of T cells in the immune response. (3 marks)

(b) The graph below shows the development of an infection with human immunodeficiency virus (HIV) over a period of ten years. Changes in the number of a type of T lymphocyte, T4 cells, are also shown.

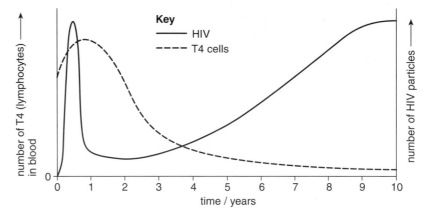

(i) Describe the changes in the number of HIV particles over the 10 year period. (3 marks)

(ii) Describe two ways in which the curve for the T4 cells differs from that for the HIV particles. (2 marks)

(iii) Suggest an explanation for the differences between the number of T4 cells in the blood and the number of HIV particles over the period. (3 marks)

(Total 11 marks)

Chapter 2

1 The diagram below shows an apple with brown rot caused by the fungus *Sclerotinia fructigena*.

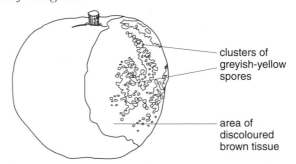

clusters of greyish-yellow spores

area of discoloured brown tissue

(a) Describe the procedure you would use to isolate and then obtain a culture of the fungus on a sterile agar plate. (3 marks)

(b) Suggest how you could show in the laboratory that the fungus you isolated was responsible for causing this brown rot in apples.

(4 marks)

(Total 7 marks)

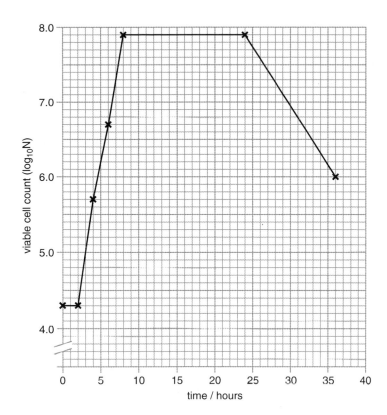

2   The graph below shows the growth curve for a population of the bacterium
    Escherichia coli in a nutrient solution. The culture was inoculated into the
    nutrient solution at time 0 and viable cell counts were made every two
    hours for 8 hours, then at 12, 24, and 36 hours. The graph is plotted as
    $\log_{10}N$ against time, where N is the total viable cell count.

(a)   (i)   In the space below calculate the number of generations
            produced during the period 4 to 8 hours after inoculation.
            Use the formula

$$n = \frac{\log_{10}N_1 - \log_{10}N_0}{\log_{10}2}$$

            where n = number of generations
                    N_0 = number of cells after 4 hours
                    N_1 = number of cells after 8 hours
                    $\log_{10}2 = 0.301$

Show your working.   (3 marks)

      (ii) Using your value calculated above, determine the exponential
            growth rate constant, k, for this period of growth of the culture.
                                                                         (1 mark)

(b)   Suggest *two* reasons for the changes in numbers of viable cells in the
      culture after being incubated for 24 hours.   (2 marks)
                                                        (Total 6 marks)

3   An experiment was carried out to investigate the growth of a certain
     species of aerobic bacterium. A broth medium containing both glucose and
     lactose was inoculated with a culture of the bacterium and maintained at a
     constant temperature of 30 °C for 24 hours. The number of viable bacterial
     cells was determined each hour using the dilution plating method.
     The results are shown in the graph below.

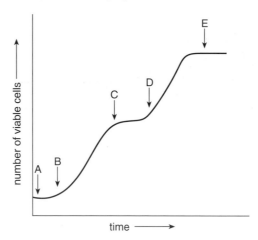

(a) Describe what is happening between points A and B on the graph.

                                                            (2 marks)

(b) Suggest explanations for the pattern of growth of the bacteria
     between each of the following time intervals.
     (i)   B to C   (2 marks)
     (ii)   C to D   (2 marks)
     (iii) D to E   (2 marks)

(c) Describe how you would carry out the dilution plating method to
     determine cell numbers.   (4 marks)

                                                (Total 12 marks)

4   Give an account of the methods of measuring the growth of
     microorganisms in culture.

                                                (Total 10 marks)

Chapter 3

1   Read through the following passage on the use of enzymes in the
     extraction of juice from fruit, then write on the dotted lines the most
     appropriate word or words to complete the account.

     Enzymes made by microorganisms may be used in commercial processes.
     In order to speed up the extraction of juice from fruit, enzymes called
     .... are used. The fruit is first .... and then the enzymes are added
     to break down the .... present in the .... These enzymes help to
     make the extracted juice ....

                                                (Total 5 marks)

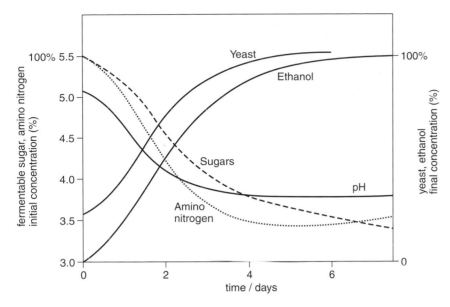

2   The graph below shows various changes which take place during the batch
    fermentation of beer.
    (a)   Explain what is meant by batch fermentation.   (3 marks)
    (b)   Explain the shape of the pH curve.   (2 marks)
    (c)   Describe the changes which take place in the quantity of amino
            nitrogen in the medium.   (4 marks)
    (d)   Explain the similarity in shape of the yeast and ethanol curves.
                                                                       (2 marks)
                                                      (Total 11 marks)

3   The sequence below shows some essential steps in the manufacture of
    yoghurt from milk.
        A.   Homogenisation of the milk (breaks up large fat globules)
        B.   Pasteurisation (heated to 72 °C for 10 seconds)
        C.   Fermentation (starter culture added)
        D.   Stirring and cooling
        E.   Addition of flavourings and colourings
        F.   Packaging

    (a)   Suggest why pasteurisation of milk is carried out.   (1 mark)

    (b)   At C, a starter culture is added to bring about the fermentation,
            during which lactose in the milk is broken down resulting in the
            formation of lactic acid. Two organisms, P and Q, are commonly used
            in starter cultures. Each one on its own is capable of bringing about
            the fermentation, but they may be used together.

            The graph overleaf shows the rate of lactic acid production when the
            two organisms are used separately (single strain cultures) and when
            they are used together (mixed strain cultures).

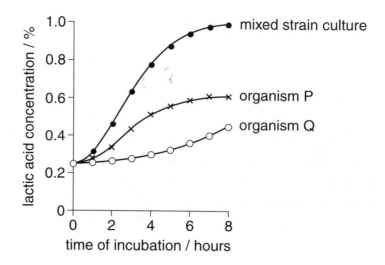

(i) Name the two organisms commonly used in starter cultures.
(2 marks)

(ii) Suggest which type of starter culture is the most suitable, giving a reason for your answer. (2 marks)

(iii) Explain the importance of the lactic acid in the production of yoghurt. (2 marks)

(iv) State why, at D, the yoghurt is cooled rapidly to 5 °C. (1 mark)

(c) (i) The activities of both organisms may be inhibited by the presence of contaminants such as antibiotics present in the milk. Suggest why antibiotics may be contaminants in milk. (1 mark)

(ii) Suggest one way in which the antibiotics could be removed from the milk (1 mark)

(d) Suggest two ways in which modern techniques have affected the way in which yoghurt is produced. (2 marks)

(Total 12 marks)

4 Give an account of the production and use of antibiotics.

(Total 10 marks)

5 Give an account of the use of microorganisms in agriculture.

(Total 10 marks)

Mark Schemes

Chapter 1

Structure	*Bacillus*	*Chlorella*	*Saccharomyces*
Cellulose cell wall	✗	✓	✗
Chloroplast	✗	✓	✗
Glycogen granules	✓	✗	✓
True nucleus	✗	✓	✓

(Total 4 marks)

2 *(a)* A: protection / maintains shape / gives support ;
   B: contains/holds genetic information / controls cell activities / eq. ;
   C: site of protein synthesis / eq. ;   (3 marks)

   (b) (i) Gram negative bacteria have a much thinner / eq. / wall (than
            Gram positive) ; wall does not retain the stain ; of crystal violet
            iodine complex ;   (2 marks)
        (ii) Escherichia / Pseudomonas / Salmonella / eq. ;   (1 mark)
                                                      (Total 6 marks)

3 crystal violet ; iodine ; ethanol / alcohol / eq. ; safranin / carbolfuchsin /
   eq. ; purple / eq. ;

                                                      (Total 5 marks)

4 *(a)* responsible for cell-mediated response ; recognise/respond to
   antigens / non-self cell ; divide to form a clone of cells ; reference to a
   named example of a T cell ; reference to function of the T cell ;
                                                          (3 marks)

   (b)

Chapter 2

1 *(a)* sterilise / flame needle scalpel loop / eq. ; remove spores / diseased
   tissue from apple ; reference to inoculation of agar plate ; careful
   lifting of lid / storage of plate ; re-sterilise needle / eq.; incubate plate
   at a suitable temperature / 10 to 30 °C.   (3 marks)

   (b) select undiseased / eq. apple ; sterilise surface / skin / eq. ; inoculate
   with fungus from culture ; reference to aseptic technique ; leave in a
   sterile / closed container ; observe for signs of disease / eq. ;
                                                          (4 marks)
                                                      (Total 7 marks)

EXAMINATION QUESTIONS

2   (a) (i) N0 5.7, N1 7.9 (both figures read correctly from graph) ;
                 2.2/0.301 ; 7.31 ;   (3 marks)
           (ii) k = 7.31/4 or k = 1.83 ;   (1 mark)
     (b) 1   lack of nutrients / lack of named nutrient ; lack of oxygen / eq. ;
                 more cells dying / no growth taking place ; accumulation of toxic
                 / eq. waste products ;   (2 marks)
                                                              (Total 6 marks)

3   (a) reference lag phase / no growth in numbers / eq. ; period of
           adjustment ; synthesis of enzymes ;   (2 marks)
     (b) (i)   reference to exponential / log growth or growth rate declines as
                 glucose is used up ; cells use glucose first ;   (2 marks)
           (ii) cells synthesising enzymes / lactase ; for metabolising lactose /
                 adapting to a new substrate ; reference to diauxic growth /
                 reference to second log phase ;   (2 marks)
           (iii) second growth phase ; cells using lactose / second substrate /
                 eq. ; decreases as lactose / nutrients used up / enters stationary
                 phase ;   (2 marks)
     (c) cell sample diluted in known volume of sterile water ; correct
           reference to serial dilution ; stated volume added to cooled, but
           molten agar / eq. ; mix, allow to solidify and incubate ; count colonies ;
           multiply by dilution factor to find original number of cells ;

                                                                          (4 marks)
     alternative scheme if samples streaked on plate: same ; same ; stated
     volume of sample on agar plate ; spreading / streaking method and
     incubation ; same ; same ;

                                                              (Total 12 marks)

4   Cell counts haemocytometer description ; known volume in each cell ;
     method of counting ; several cells counted for mean ; correct method for
     calculation of population ;
     Dilution plating serial dilution ; counts viable cells ; use of sterile saline /
     eq. ; specific correct dilution e.g. 1:9 ; plate out stated volume ; correct
     method for calculating population ;
     Mass of sample use known volume ; distribution standardised before taking
     sample ; centrifuge / filtering reference ; drying ; weigh pellet / weigh
     residue ; correct method for calculation of population ;
     Turbidity use of standard cell / cuvette ; how reading taken / comment on
     use of colorimeter eq. ; compare with known standards ; read from
     standard graph ;
     General point measurements taken at start and finish ; at two different times ;
     comment on total cell counts and viable cell counts ; credit reference to other
     suitable method e.g. coulter counter ;

Chapter 3

1   pectinases / cellulases ; chopped up / eq. ; pectin / cellulose ; cell walls ;
    clearer / clarified / eq. ;

(Total 5 marks)

2   *(a)*   fermentation in closed container ; (microorganism in container) with
            nutrient medium / eq. ; left for fermentation to take place ; nothing is
            added / removed while process taking place ; except venting waste
            gases ; product is separated / harvested / collected at the end of the
            process / reference to downstream processing   (3 marks)

    (b)   falls steeply / eq. while fermentation is rapid / while yeast is
            reproducing / eq. quickly / during log phase ; CO_2 is being produced /
            acid gas / forms carbonic acid ; falls more slowly as the activity of the
            yeast diminishes / eq. ;   (2 marks)

    (c)   falls for first 3/4 days / during log phase /initial fermentation /as yeast
            increases ; being used up in growth of yeast / for proteins / amino
            acids / DNA ; levels out until about day 6 / accept from 4 to 6 days ;
            breakdown of dead yeast cells releasing amino nitrogen ;   (4 marks)

    (d)   ethanol produced by (the metabolism of yeast ; rapid production of
            ethanol during log phase of yeast growth / eq. ; no further production
            of ethanol when plateau reached / eq. ; fermentable sugar has been
            used up ;   (2 marks)

(Total 11 marks)

3   *(a)*   to kill pathogenic microorganisms / bacteria / eq. ;

    (b)   (i)   1 Streptococcus or Lactococcus / thermophilus ; 2 Lactobacillus
                   bulgaricus ;   (2 marks)

            (ii)   mixed strain / eq. ; more / faster rate of lactic acid production /
                   OR reference to synergism / mutualistic / symbiotic / relationship ;
                                                                   (2 marks)

            (iii) reduces the pH to 4.6 / 4.7 ; casein / milk protein coagulates at
                   this pH ; yoghurt thickens ; gives characteristic taste / flavour ;
                                                                   (2 marks)

            (iv)   inhibit / reduce the activity of the bacteria / OR reduce / eq.
                   production of lactic acid ;   (1 mark)

    (c)   (i)   used to treat mastitis / disease / illness in cows / eq. / given in
                   food ;   (1 mark)

            (ii)   use enzymes / penicillinase to break them down ;   (1 mark)

    (d)   1   pure / reliable cultures of lactase-fermenting bacteria obtainable ;
                 can control temperature more accurately ; 2 acidity / pH can be
                 measured by probes / eq. ; better sterilisation techniques /
                 improved equipment / eq. ; better types of starter culture / OR
                 reference to use of different types of milk;   (2 marks)

(Total 12 marks)

4   antibiotics inhibit growth of / kill microorganisms / bacteria / eq ; (mostly) produced by fungi ; named e.g. of fungus and antibiotic ; as secondary metabolites ; credit some explanation of secondary metabolite / eq. ; produced (commercially) by batch culture / fermentation ; sterile / eq. medium / reference to sterile conditions at any stage ; large (volume) fermenter / large volume of medium ; reference to any two controlled conditions, e.g. temperature / pH / acidity / alkalinity / oxygen ; production monitored so that stopped when maximum levels present ; medium filtered off / reference to downstream processing ; any reference to subsequent modification / purification ; when used as drugs exploit differences between prokaryotes and eukaryotes / eq. ; may be bactericidal / eq. ; or bacteriostatic / eq. ; host organisms defences immune system then kill the pathogens ; can cause (bacterial cell) wall disruption / eq. ; e.g. penicillin / most antibiotics on Gram poistive bacteria ; disrupt cell membranes by affecting permeability ; e.g. tetracyclines / eq. disrupt (bacterial) protein synthesis ; prevent tRNA binding to 70S ribosomes / eq. credit reference to development of resistance / reference to use of broad and narrow spectrum antibiotics / eq. ; use in farming qualified e.g. to increase yield / eq. ;

5   lactic acid bacteria / Lactobacillus / Ecosyl / eq. used to produce silage ; sugars converted to lactic acid ; lowers pH / pH to 4 - 4.5 ; prevents further microbial deterioration / eq. / reference to use of Ecobale / eq. to inhibit mould growth ; use of Agrobacterium to introduce new genes into plants ; via Ti plasmid ; credit examples of genetic modification of crop plants, with reasons for adding new genes ; inoculate crops with Rhizobium to boost N-fixation ; detail of inoculation method, e.g. coat seeds ; can grow more crops eq. in N-deficient soil / less use of N-fertilisers ; differ in N-fixing ability / host specificity ; plasmids used to transfer characteristics between Rhizobium species ; some fungi attack insects / eq. ; produce an enzyme which destroys exoskeleton / relevant detail ; reference to production of microbial insecticide for Bacillus thuringiensis ; effective against caterpillars / insects ; use of a virus to control insects / eq. ; comment on use of microorganisms in composting ; comment on use of microorganisms in biogas ; comment on use of microorganisms in conversion of straw to alcohol ; reference to use of cyanobacteria to fix nitrogen, particularly in paddy fields to increase yield ; reference to production of SCP for animal foodstuffs ; credit further details of SCP production ;

Index

INDEX